Piney Grove Church

Creek

Cemetery

Mount Harmony Church

Swanpond

Branch

Cemetery

Cruze

PIKE

PLAINS

PLAINS

Dora Kennedy School

STRAW

Creek

1000

900

VABM 891

Marbledale Church

Water

Abandoned

Water

Marbledale School

Marbledale

BM 867

Paint Rock Bluff

FRENCI

Mile 4

24000

1 MILE

4000    5000    6000    7000 FEET

1 KILOMETER

BCHj

AL MAP ACCURACY STANDARDS

JRVEY, WASHINGTON, D. C. 20242,

HATTANOOGA OR KNOXVILLE, TENN.,

OLOGY, NASHVILLE, TENNESSEE

AND SYMBOLS IS AVAILABLE ON REQUEST

ILL. KENTUCKY
MO.
TENNESSEE    N.C.
MISS.  ALA.  GA.  S.C.

QUADRANGLE LOCATION

(TVA 147-NE)

ROAD CLASSIFICATION

In developed areas, only through roads are classified

HARD-SURFACE ALL WEATHER ROADS        DRY WEATHER ROADS

Heavy-duty.                 1 LANE 16 LANE   Improved dirt.
Medium-duty.            1 LANE 16 LANE       Unimproved dirt
Loose-surface, graded, or narrow hard-surface

70  U. S. Route        100  State Route

SHOOKS GAP, TENN.

N3552.5—W8345/7.5

1953

AMS 4255 IV NE—SERIES V841

Crystals of tourmaline (right) and quartz, from Pala, California.

# Discovering
# Rocks and Minerals

A NATURE AND SCIENCE GUIDE TO
THEIR COLLECTION AND IDENTIFICATION

by ROY A. GALLANT
and CHRISTOPHER J. SCHUBERTH

PUBLISHED FOR THE AMERICAN MUSEUM OF NATURAL HISTORY

 THE NATURAL HISTORY PRESS

GARDEN CITY, NEW YORK

*For Jonathan, James,*
*Karin and Paul*

The authors' thanks to Harriet Cole, the designer of this book,
and to Joseph M. Sedacca and his staff at The American Museum
of Natural History for preparing the many diagrams.

The Natural History Press, publisher for The American Museum
of Natural History, is a division of Doubleday & Company, Inc.
Directed by a joint editorial board made up of members of the
staff of both the Museum and Doubleday, the Natural History Press
publishes books and periodicals in all branches of the
life and earth sciences, including anthropology and astronomy.
The Natural History Press has its editorial offices at
The American Museum of Natural History, Central Park West
at 79th Street, New York, New York 10024, and its business
offices at 501 Franklin Avenue, Garden City, New York.

# CONTENTS

## TABLES AND CHARTS

# ABOUT THIS BOOK

*Discovering Rocks and Minerals* has been planned and written for beginning collectors and for seasoned "rock hounds" of all ages. It has also been written for the person who has more than just a casual interest in the "Rocks that Make Our Landscape," as one chapter is called.

If you happen to be an impatient type and want to rush off on a field trip without preparing for it, fine. The chapter "How to Collect Rocks and Minerals" will get you started and give you many tips on where and how to collect. But if you have had the disappointing experience of rushing into rock collecting without knowing much about what you were collecting, you would probably recommend a more systematic approach. We certainly do.

If you are the second kind of person, then this is your kind of book. We have planned it in the most logical way we could think of. The first chapter gives you a sweeping view of the Earth's crust—when and how it was formed, the near endless variety of rocks and minerals composing it, and the forces throughout geologic time that have given the crust the form and structure it has today. The next two chapters are about minerals and rocks: minerals first, simply because they are the building blocks of rocks. Another chapter shows you how to identify 18 common rocks and 26 common minerals by using identification keys, which, to our knowledge, do not appear in this form in any other book. This is an important chapter, for beginners and seasoned collectors alike. If the seasoned collector wants to know about the mineral make-up of a rock sample or the simplified chemistry of a mineral, he will find that information in the several tables appearing in this book.

A chapter about fossils—what they are, how they are formed, and how and where to collect them—has been included in this book for the good reason that fossils play an important part in the long geologic history of our planet. The concluding chapter, "Telling Geologic Time," places in time the materials of the Earth's crust and the various agents and forces that have affected them. A rock that you casually pick up and skim across a pond on a lazy summer afternoon may have been formed millions of years ago and carried by tide and time to the field or beach where you found it. To know its history is, in a way, to know a little more about yourself. That, really, is what this book is all about.

ROY A. GALLANT
CHRISTOPHER J. SCHUBERTH
*The American Museum of Natural History*

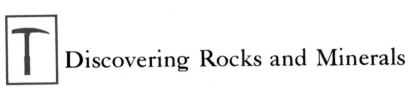

Discovering Rocks and Minerals

Mountains, which are thrust up by forces deep beneath the Earth's crust, seem eternal, but they are not. Active volcanoes, like this one in Japan, are reminders that the Earth is an ever-changing planet.

# 1    The Planet Earth

The Earth is an ever-changing planet. Since it was formed some five billion or so years ago, out of the gas and dust of space, our planet has developed a rocky crust, an atmosphere, seas, mountains, glaciers, and the endless variety of plants and animals that live on its surface. To us, these features seem unchanging and everlasting. During the Cretaceous Period in the Earth's history (65 to 136 million years ago), what are now the craggy ranges of the Rocky Mountains were thrust skyward by powerful forces within the Earth. To our eyes today these towering peaks of rock seem eternal. But they are not. The slow, endless process of erosion is continually wearing them away. Millions of years from now the Rocky Mountains will be old mountains, as rounded and weather-worn as the Appalachians, which were formed more than 200 million years ago.

The seas, too, seem eternal, yet there was a time when there were no seas on the Earth. After the oceans formed, different parts of the continents were flooded at different times. During the Ordovician Period (440 to 500 million years ago) shallow seas covered much of Europe and more than half of North America. Parts of Oregon and California were covered by shallow seas 150 million years ago when the dinosaurs roamed the Earth, long before man came into being. Although these long-term changes are much too slow for us to observe, they have left their "calling-cards" in the rocks. A rock you hold in your hand may contain evidence of the existence of a shallow inland sea and the life that it harbored millions of years ago. In later chapters of this book, you will discover how to read the mineral and rock records, and how to interpret the fascinating stories they have to tell.

Other changes on the Earth's surface do not take millions of years; they occur before our eyes. Within a few years, or a few months, or even a few days, we can see dramatic sculpturing of the Earth. An undersea volcano erupts and overnight gives birth to an island. A meandering river, always seeking the lowest land, may change its course over a period of only a few years, producing new land features. The oxbow lakes in Texas are cutoff loops of the meandering Rio Grande. The Mississippi River delta, the land on which New Orleans is built, is changing day by day, year by year. Sand, mud, and other sediments carried along by the river are constantly being dumped at the river mouth, enlarging old fingers of land and forming new ones. This land-building process is an example of the land gaining over the

This oxbow lake near Weslaco, Texas, was once a loop of the Rio Grande. The loop was cut off when the river changed course, and a lake was left.

Most astronomers think that the Sun, planets, and their satellites were formed out of a vast cloud of gas and dust some five billion years ago.

sea. In other areas the sea is gaining over the land. Parts of the coast of England, for example, are being worn away by the pounding sea at the rate of about 17 feet a year.

Change, then, is one thing we can be certain of. The mountains, the seas, the deserts, the plains in some small way will be different tomorrow from what they are today. The nature of the changes—how and when they take place—is an endless puzzle which geologists and other scientists are ever trying to solve.

### The Earth in space

The scientist's task would be much easier if he knew just *how* the Earth was formed some five billion or so years ago. In the past there have been many attempts to explain how the Sun and its planets came into being. The American astronomer Gerard Kuiper paints this picture:

The Solar System began as a great dark cloud of dust and gas which stretched about 9 billion miles from edge to edge. Gradually it closed in on

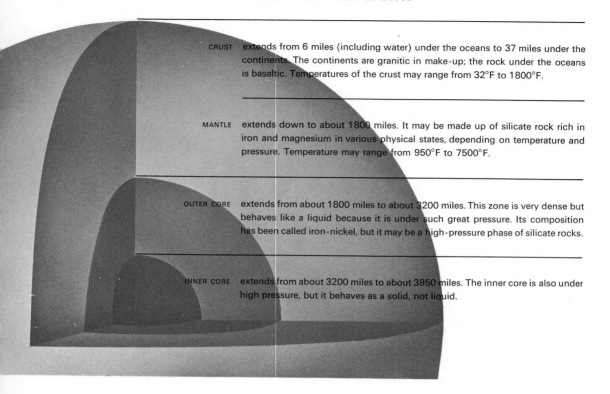

CRUST extends from 6 miles (including water) under the oceans to 37 miles under the continents. The continents are granitic in make-up; the rock under the oceans is basaltic. Temperatures of the crust may range from 32°F to 1800°F.

MANTLE extends down to about 1800 miles. It may be made up of silicate rock rich in iron and magnesium in various physical states, depending on temperature and pressure. Temperature may range from 950°F to 7500°F.

OUTER CORE extends from about 1800 miles to about 3200 miles. This zone is very dense but behaves like a liquid because it is under such great pressure. Its composition has been called iron-nickel, but it may be a high-pressure phase of silicate rocks.

INNER CORE extends from about 3200 miles to about 3950 miles. The inner core is also under high pressure, but it behaves as a solid, not liquid.

itself, spinning and flattening out, and eventually became a huge rotating disk. About 95 percent of the cloud's gas and dust formed a sphere at the center of the disk. The sphere became the Sun. In its early days the Sun was much larger and cooler than it is today. It glowed a dull red and was large enough to fill the space within Mercury's present orbit. Spread around the new Sun was a circular disk of "leftover" gas and dust. This great wheel of material reached outward from the Sun's equator to a distance of about 3 billion miles. Within it, whirlpools formed, broke up, and formed again. But some of the whirls—the larger and stronger ones—did not break up. Those that held together swept up more gas and dust and grew larger and larger. At least eight such whirls formed and grew. Eventually each one formed into a sphere and, over millions of years, condensed, hardened, and became one of the planets.

Just as the new Sun had a disk of gas and dust spinning around it, so did each planet. The material circling the planets developed whirls which became the satellites of the planets. Just as the planets are spread out in line with the Sun's equator, most of the satellites are spread out in line with their parent planet's equator. But no one can say for certain if that is the way the Sun, the planets and their satellites actually were formed. However, many astronomers feel that until a better explanation comes along, Kuiper's idea is a good one.

At one stage in our planet's history the Earth may have been a molten sphere of rock and metal. If so, the heavier materials, such as iron and nickel, would have sunk slowly toward the center of the new Earth. Meanwhile, lighter materials, such as those containing the silicates, would have risen toward the surface. (Most of the rock exposed on the Earth's surface today is made up of silicate minerals.) Over many, many years, the hot materials at and near the surface would have cooled enough to form a solid, rocky crust, the crust which we walk upon today.

Although many scientists think that the Earth originally was a molten sphere of rock, others feel that it was not that hot. Possibly it never went through a molten stage during its early history. Much more evidence is needed before we can say with any certainty how the Earth was formed.

### Formation of the atmosphere

The Earth's original atmosphere was not like the air we breathe today. It probably contained some water vapor, ammonia gas, and methane (marsh gas). If it did, energy from the Sun would have broken up the water vapor into free oxygen and hydrogen. Because it is so light, the hydrogen would slowly have leaked away into space, but the heavier oxygen would have remained. Unlike the more massive planets (such as Jupiter), which have free hydrogen in their atmospheres, the Earth does not have appreciable amounts of free hydrogen in its atmosphere today. Oxygen also would combine with the methane, changing it into carbon dioxide and more water vapor.

If this process actually took place in the atmosphere, something else would have been happening to the young Earth. Heat beneath the crust would have caused many chemical reactions to take place within the Earth. Over millions of years the hot Earth would have released great amounts of steam, water, carbon dioxide, carbon monoxide, nitrogen and other gases. Still later, when many volcanoes formed, there must have been great outpourings of carbon dioxide, and nitrogen. The nitrogen making up the bulk of our atmosphere today, says Kuiper, probably came from a long period of volcanic eruptions.

### Formation of the seas

The birth of the oceans, like the birth of the Earth itself, may forever remain a mystery. However, scientists think that the oceans, which cover 70.8 per cent of the Earth's surface, might have been formed the following way:

Long before the dawn of life on our planet, when the hardening crust may still have been very hot, great gushers of steam, nitrogen, and other gases were rising into the air. As the water vapor rose to cold regions of the upper atmosphere, it cooled, changed into liquid water, and fell to the surface as rain. But the great masses of rocks were not yet cool enough for the rain to settle on them. As torrents of water poured down on the hot crust, the water was instantly heated and changed into steam. Then the steam was driven back into the upper regions of the atmosphere again.

At this time in the Earth's history, and for thousands or millions of years to come, storm clouds must have blanketed our planet completely, just as Venus' clouds blanket that planet today. Sunlight could not reach the Earth's surface. But gradually, as the primeval rocky surface cooled, the rains fell and remained as water. Streams, then rivers washed over the planet, etching their way down mountains and across rocky plains, the water always seeking the lowest levels.

For tens of millions of years the rains continued to fall and flow into shallow depressions and great trenches, gradually forming seas. As the rivers and streams washed over the land, they picked up, dissolved, and carried salts with them. Over the centuries, as the surface water of the oceans evaporated and fell again as rain, the salts remained behind, accumulating in the seas, as they are accumulating today.

Eventually, after how many dark centuries we do not know, the great rains eased and stopped. Dim light began shining through the thinning clouds and one day the Sun's rays broke through, illuminating a planet of jagged rock and blue water.

**The first life forms**

At least two billion years ago, at a time when the Earth's atmosphere was very different from today's, the first "living things" came into being. They were formed out of simple chemical materials of the atmosphere (such as hydrogen, methane, ammonia, and water vapor) and accumulated in the primeval seas and lakes. These earliest life forms were not any of the living things we see today. They were complex arrangements of certain molecules, different from other molecules in a very special way: by combining with other chemicals around them they were able to produce new molecules exactly like themselves. During the next 1½ billion years or so, these earliest life forms gave rise to more complex ones—the great-great-grandparents of the plants and animals living today. With the appearance of simple plants some 1½ billion or more years ago, the Earth's atmosphere gradually became enriched with oxygen. As green plants around us today enrich the atmosphere with oxygen through the process of photosynthesis, so did the primitive green plants more than a billion years ago. The *basic* make-up of the air today is most likely very nearly the same as it was half a billion years ago, yet in small ways it is constantly changing now as it has changed in the past. Volcanoes and man's factories and machines are constantly pouring gases into the air. The weathering of rocks also releases gases, as does the atmosphere's interaction with the oceans. Like the soft sediments of the land, which are changed to rock, the atmosphere, too, has changed over the centuries. Yet the *relative* amounts of nitrogen, oxygen, water vapor, carbon dioxide, and other gases of the air have changed very little over the past hundreds of million years.

Let us now turn our attention to that part of the Earth that interests rock collectors most—the Earth's thin crust. As the diagram on page 12 shows, if the crust were stripped away from the Earth completely, our planet would be only slightly smaller. Yet, it is in this thin crust, on the average only 25 miles thick, that all of the rock- and mineral-forming processes that we will be talking about take place.

Intergrown cubic crystals of fluorite, a calcium fluoride mineral.

# 2 Minerals—the Building Blocks of Rocks

Have you ever heard the word "mineral" used in different ways? A druggist may use the word when he tells you that a certain pill is rich in vitamins and "minerals." In the game "Animal, Vegetable, or Mineral," a mineral is anything that is neither vegetable nor animal. To the geologist, the word "mineral" has a special meaning. To him, minerals are the building blocks of rocks; so before you can understand the many ways rocks differ from each other, you must first learn a few things about minerals.

### Elements—the building blocks of minerals

Because minerals are made of certain chemical substances called "elements," we should begin our account of minerals with a few words about elements and atoms.

Centuries ago the Greek philosophers discussed the "stuff," or matter, that makes up the Earth. One of them, a man named Democritus, who lived around 450 B.C., used the word "atom" to describe the tiniest possible piece of matter which he could imagine. Democritus felt that different kinds of things—water and rocks, for example—must be made of different kinds of atoms. He imagined some atoms as being slippery and smooth, and others as being rough. The idea that there are atoms—pieces of matter much too small to be seen—has lasted down through the centuries.

Today we know that in some ways Democritus was right. Even though we still cannot see an atom, we know that there are many different kinds. Yet all atoms have certain things in common. For example, all have a central core, called the **nucleus**, and one or more tiny particles, called **electrons**, circling the nucleus.

The simplest of the many different kinds of atoms is an atom of hydrogen (see diagram). Its nucleus is made up of one particle called a **proton**, and one electron circles the nucleus. Helium, the next simplest element, has two protons and two other particles, called **neutrons**, forming its nucleus. Circling its

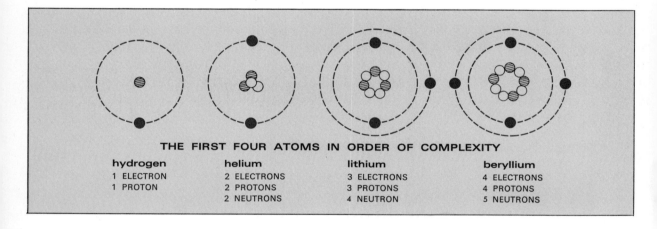

### THE FIRST FOUR ATOMS IN ORDER OF COMPLEXITY

| hydrogen | helium | lithium | beryllium |
|---|---|---|---|
| 1 ELECTRON | 2 ELECTRONS | 3 ELECTRONS | 4 ELECTRONS |
| 1 PROTON | 2 PROTONS | 3 PROTONS | 4 PROTONS |
| | 2 NEUTRONS | 4 NEUTRON | 5 NEUTRONS |

nucleus are two electrons. Since the nucleus of helium contains two protons and two neutrons, it is heavier than the nucleus of hydrogen. You can see that atoms of lithium and beryllium have still more protons and neutrons in their cores, and still more electrons circling the nucleus. If we kept on examining the many different kinds of atoms, we would find that 103 have been discovered so far. As the different kinds of atoms are arranged from number 1 to number 103, they become heavier and heavier toward number 103.

They become heavier simply because they have more protons and neutrons packed into the nucleus. An atom of gold, for instance, is heavier than an atom of hydrogen, helium, lithium, or beryllium because each atom of gold has 79 protons and 118 neutrons in its nucleus, giving it a weight of (79 + 118) 197. Yet, there are atoms still heavier than gold. A uranium atom, for example, has a weight of 238.

A collection of many atoms that are all *exactly* alike forms a substance we call an **element**. Every one of the billions upon billions of atoms making up a bar of gold is exactly like every other atom in the bar. That is why gold is an element. The smallest possible piece of an element is one of its atoms. Wood is not an element because it is made of many, many *different* kinds of atoms. Because there are 103 different kinds of atoms known to us, there are at least 103 different elements; among them are copper, silver, oxygen, iron, and uranium. A few elements, such as oxygen, hydrogen, and helium are gases; others are solids, such as gold and sulfur; and one, mercury, is a liquid.

### What are minerals?

On page 26 we have listed the 103 elements. You will notice that 10 of them are printed in heavy type. These 10 are alike in two ways: 1. They are solid elements; and 2. they are commonly found in nature in a pure state.

We can now begin to say what a mineral is. Any solid element found free in nature (including mercury, although it is a liquid) is a mineral. But without too much work you can look through the list of 103 elements and find many solid ones that are not in heavy type—iron and lead, for instance. These also are minerals because they are solid elements. The only reason we have not printed them in heavy type is that they are not *commonly* found in their pure state in nature; usually they are combined with some other element or elements. It may surprise you to learn that pure iron is quite rare in the Earth's crust.

If the 10 elements in heavy type were the *only* minerals, the rocks we find along the roadside, in the mountains, and along a beach would show very little mineral variety. But the rocks of the Earth's crust do show much mineral variety in their makeup, so certainly there must be more than 10 minerals.

Actually there are about 2000 minerals that have been studied by mineralogists. That means that most minerals must be made of more than one element. When one element combines with one or more other elements a **compound** is formed. For example, when oxygen and hydrogen combine they form the compound we call water. While only a few of the many different kinds of minerals are a single, solid element, most minerals are combinations of elements, or compounds. But not all compounds are minerals—only those that were formed by a chemical, not a biological, process. Let's take a close look at such a compound, one that you eat every day—the mineral **halite,** which is common table salt.

Halite is made of the two elements sodium and chlorine. Like all other minerals made of one or more elements, halite has its atoms arranged in a fixed (geometric) pattern. If you look at several tiny pieces of halite through a magnifying glass, or under a hand lens, you will see that each piece has the general shape of a cube. If you crushed one of the tiny cubes it would break apart into many more pieces, and each of those pieces would also be a cube. If you could keep on breaking the cubes into smaller and smaller cubes, eventually you would end up with the smallest possible halite cube—one with 14 chlorine atoms and 13 sodium atoms. When enough of these tiny cubes are locked together, your eye sees their cube shape. Such regular shapes

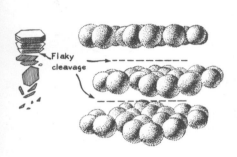

Here is a glass model of the largest diamond ever found, the 3106-carat Cullinan, and a natural, uncut 17-carat diamond crystal. The diamond crystal is compared with graphite, the only other mineral form of the element carbon. The great variation in hardness and other physical properties of diamond and graphite is due to the difference in their atomic structures (shown in color). As the pencil moves, layers of graphite slip off. Because each carbon atom in diamond is bonded to four others in a rigid crystal form, diamond does not break apart easily.

made by atoms arranged in a fixed pattern, and visible to the naked eye, are called **crystals**. Crystals of minerals, such as those on pages 20 and 21, are seldom found on collecting trips, so don't expect to have such specimens in your collection, not right away at least. The illustrations on this page show the atoms, and their fixed patterns, forming the minerals diamond and graphite.

So, a few minerals are solid elements that occur free in nature, but most minerals are compounds of two or more elements. The atoms of all minerals have a fixed pattern. Sometimes you may be lucky enough to see this fixed geometric arrangement without magnification as a crystal. And finally, each mineral has its own definite composition and was formed by a chemical process.

**Some important rock-forming minerals**

In a book as short as this one, we cannot describe each of the 2000 known minerals. What we will do, then, is talk about only those that make up certain kinds of rocks. About 30 common minerals make up almost all of the rocks we see on the Earth's surface. Of the 103 elements, only eight of them *commonly* combine with each other and form mineral compounds. Oxygen is one, and makes up 46.6 per cent, by weight, of the Earth's crust; silicon, another element, makes up 27.7 per cent. The remaining six elements, in the order of abundance, are aluminum, iron, calcium, sodium, potassium, and magnesium. These eight elements alone make up just a little less than 99 per cent, by weight, of the Earth's crust, so they are the building blocks of most of the minerals. And, as you might guess, by far the most minerals contain oxygen and silicon. These are the minerals—the oxygen- and silicon-containing ones—that we are most concerned about in this book. They are the ones you are most likely to find on collecting trips. They are called **silicate minerals.**

The silicate minerals are broken down into smaller groups, as shown in the "Family Tree of Minerals" on pages 22 and 23. Those silicate minerals that have iron and magnesium are called **ferromagnesian** silicates, or **mafic** minerals. (They include the important rock-forming minerals augite, hornblende, olivine, and biotite mica.) Silicate minerals that do not contain iron and magnesium are called **nonferromagnesian** silicates, or **felsic** minerals. These include the important rock-forming minerals quartz, the feldspars, and muscovite mica. (Additional mineral groups are also shown.)

We have also listed on pages 24 and 25 all of the minerals mentioned in this book, together with their crystal shapes. If you want to find out what "class" of mineral olivine belongs to, for example, first locate it on the Family Tree. You will find that it is a ferromagnesian silicate because it contains the elements iron and magnesium. If you want to know still more about the chemical makeup of olivine, again turn to the Building Blocks table on pages 24 and 25. By reading the numbers following the word "olivine," you will find the four elements that olivine contains. A colored number following a mineral means that the mineral *always* contains atoms of the element (Si and O in olivine, for instance) with the same number; a black number following a mineral means that the mineral may or may not contain the numbered element.

The chemistry of minerals, which we have been describing in this chapter, may not interest you if you are a beginning collector. But if you intend to become a serious collector of rocks and minerals there will come a time when you will need to know something about the chemistry of your specimens. For that reason we have included this chapter in the book. Let us now turn to the rocks that make up the Earth's crust. Rocks, as you will discover, contain many different combinations of minerals.

This upper part of a large quartz crystal from Auburn, Maine, shows that crystals are symmetrically sided solids bounded by plane surfaces. The plane surfaces are the visible outward form of a regularly repeated arrangement of atoms.

A cluster of slender hexagonal-shaped crystals of colorless quartz, called "rock crystal," from Hot Springs, Arkansas.

Several crystals of orthoclase feldspar.

These well-developed garnet crystals from Stikine River, Alaska, show the commonly occurring rhombic dodecahedron (large diamond-shaped faces) and the smaller tetragonal trisoctahedron crystal faces.

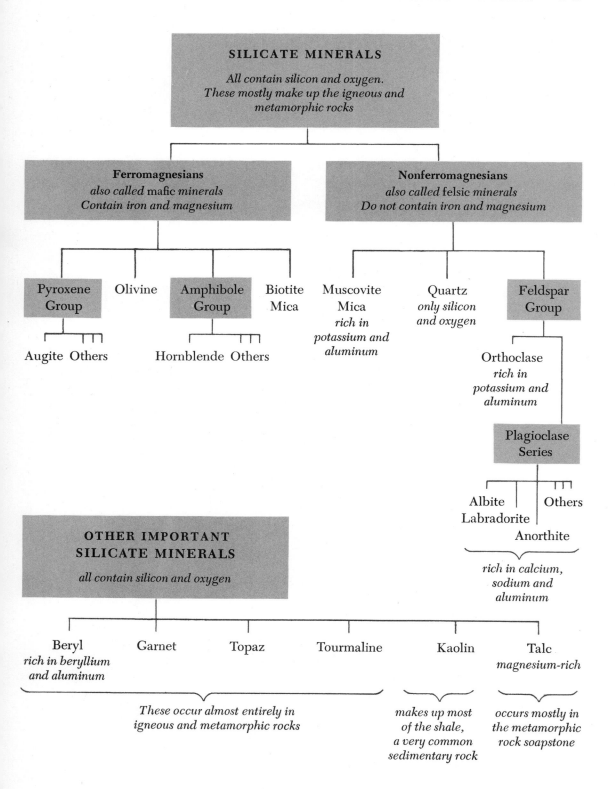

SILICATE MINERALS

*All contain silicon and oxygen.
These mostly make up the igneous and
metamorphic rocks*

**Ferromagnesians**
*also called* mafic *minerals*
*Contain iron and magnesium*

**Nonferromagnesians**
*also called* felsic *minerals*
*Do not contain iron and magnesium*

Pyroxene Group

Olivine

Amphibole Group

Biotite Mica

Muscovite Mica
*rich in
potassium and
aluminum*

Quartz
*only silicon
and oxygen*

Feldspar Group

Augite   Others

Hornblende   Others

Orthoclase
*rich in
potassium and
aluminum*

Plagioclase Series

Albite
Labradorite
Anorthite

Others

*rich in calcium,
sodium and
aluminum*

**OTHER IMPORTANT
SILICATE MINERALS**

*all contain silicon and oxygen*

Beryl
*rich in beryllium
and aluminum*

Garnet

Topaz

Tourmaline

Kaolin

Talc
*magnesium-rich*

*These occur almost entirely in
igneous and metamorphic rocks*

*makes up most
of the shale,
a very common
sedimentary rock*

*occurs mostly in
the metamorphic
rock soapstone*

# COMMON MINERALS

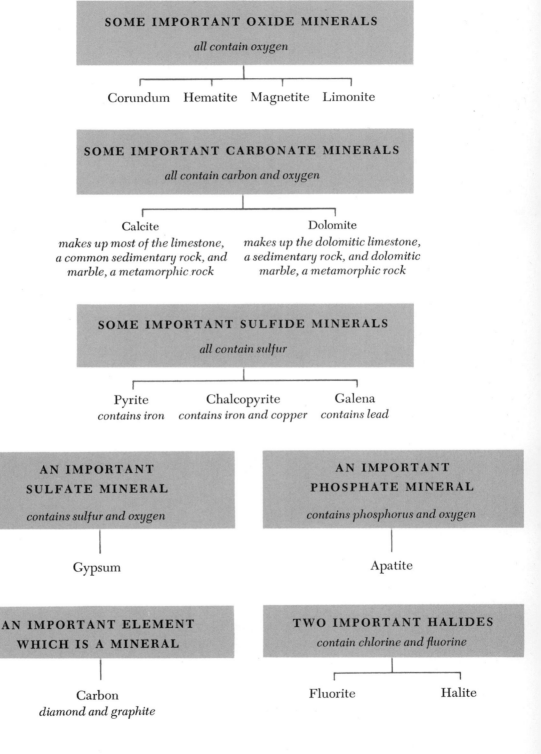

**SOME IMPORTANT OXIDE MINERALS**

*all contain oxygen*

Corundum   Hematite   Magnetite   Limonite

**SOME IMPORTANT CARBONATE MINERALS**

*all contain carbon and oxygen*

Calcite
*makes up most of the limestone, a common sedimentary rock, and marble, a metamorphic rock*

Dolomite
*makes up the dolomitic limestone, a sedimentary rock, and dolomitic marble, a metamorphic rock*

**SOME IMPORTANT SULFIDE MINERALS**

*all contain sulfur*

Pyrite
*contains iron*

Chalcopyrite
*contains iron and copper*

Galena
*contains lead*

**AN IMPORTANT SULFATE MINERAL**

*contains sulfur and oxygen*

Gypsum

**AN IMPORTANT PHOSPHATE MINERAL**

*contains phosphorus and oxygen*

Apatite

**AN IMPORTANT ELEMENT WHICH IS A MINERAL**

Carbon
*diamond and graphite*

**TWO IMPORTANT HALIDES**
*contain chlorine and fluorine*

Fluorite   Halite

# THE BUILDING BLOCKS

## ELEMENTS

| | | | | |
|---|---|---|---|---|
| ALUMINUM | 1 | | IRON | 11 |
| BERYLLIUM | 2 | | LEAD | 12 |
| BORON | 3 | | LITHIUM | 13 |
| CALCIUM | 4 | | MAGNESIUM | 14 |
| CARBON | 5 | | MANGANESE | 15 |
| CESIUM | 6 | | OXYGEN | 16 |
| CHLORINE | 7 | | POTASSIUM | 17 |
| COPPER | 8 | | SILICON | 18 |
| FLUORINE | 9 | | SODIUM | 19 |
| HYDROXL GROUP 10 (a combination of one atom of hydrogen and one atom of oxygen) | | | SULFUR | 20 |
| | | | TITANIUM | 21 |
| | | | WATER (a compound) | 22 |

A
TETRAGONAL

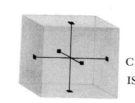

SIDE VIEW

B MONOCLINIC

C
ISOMETRIC
cubic

D
ORTHORHOMBIC

E
TRICLINIC

F
HEXAGONAL

## MINERALS

| CRYSTAL SYSTEM[1] | MINERALS | ELEMENTS[2] |
|---|---|---|
| F | Apatite | 4, **7**, **9**, 16 |
| B | Augite | 1, 4, **11**, **14**, 16, 18 |
| F | Beryl | 1, 2, **6**, **13**, 16, 18, **19** |
| B | Biotite (*a mica*) | 1, 10, **11**, **14**, 16, 17, 18 |
| F | Calcite | 4, 5, 16 |
| A | Chalcopyrite | 8, 11, 20 |
| F | Corundum (*ruby and Sapphire*) | 1, 16 |
| C | Diamond | 5 |
| F | Dolomite | 4, 5, 14, 16 |
| B, E | Feldspar Group | 1, 4, 16, **17**, 18, **19** |
| C | Fluorite | 4, 9 |
| C | Galena | 12, 20 |
| C | Garnet | **1**, **4**, **11**, **14**, **15**, 16, 18 |
| F | Graphite | 5 |
| B | Gypsum | 4, 16, 20, 22 |
| C | Halite (*salt*) | 7, 19 |
| F | Hematite | 11, 16 |
| B | Hornblende | **1**, 4, **10**, **11**, **14**, 16, 18, 19, **21** |
| B | Kaolin (*a clay mineral*) | 1, 10, 16, 18 |
| (amorphous) | Limonite | 10, 11, 16, 22 |
| C | Magnetite | 11, 16 |
| B | Muscovite (*a mica*) | 1, 10, 16, 17, 18 |
| D | Olivine | **11**, **14**, 16, 18 |
| C | Pyrite (*also called fool's gold*) | 11, 20 |
| F | Quartz | 16, 18 |
| B | Talc | 10, 14, 16, 18 |
| D | Topaz | 1, **9**, **10**, 16, 18 |
| F | Tourmaline | 1, 3, 4, **9**, **11**, **13**, **14**, 16, 18, **19** |

[1] The letter preceding the name of each mineral designates the mineral's crystal type. Six crystal types are shown on opposite page.

[2] The numbers following the name of each mineral designate the elements present in the mineral. The numbers in heavy type show that the element is only sometimes present in the mineral.

# THE CHEMICAL ELEMENTS

*Those printed in heavy type are commonly*
*occurring solid elements that are also minerals.*

| ELEMENT | SYMBOL | ELEMENT | SYMBOL | ELEMENT | SYMBOL |
|---|---|---|---|---|---|
| Actinium | Ac | Hafnium | Hf | Promethium | Pm |
| Aluminum | Al | Helium | He | Protactinium | Pa |
| Americium | Am | Holmium | Ho | Radium | Ra |
| **Antimony** | **Sb** | Hydrogen | H | Radon | Rn |
| Argon | A | Indium | In | Rhenium | Re |
| **Arsenic** | **As** | Iodine | I | Rhodium | Rh |
| Astatine | At | Iridium | Ir | Rubidium | Rb |
| Barium | Ba | Iron | Fe | Ruthenium | Ru |
| Berkelium | Bk | Krypton | Kr | Samarium | Sm |
| Beryllium | Be | Lanthanum | La | Scandium | Sc |
| **Bismuth** | **Bi** | Lawrencium | Lw | Selenium | Se |
| Boron | B | Lead | Pb | Silicon | Si |
| Bromine | Br | Lithium | Li | **Silver** | **Ag** |
| Cadmium | Cd | Lutetium | Lu | Sodium | Na |
| Calcium | Ca | Magnesium | Mg | Strontium | Sr |
| Californium | Cf | Manganese | Mn | **Sulfur** | **S** |
| **Carbon** | **C** | Mendelevium | Mv | Tantalum | Ta |
| Cerium | Ce | Mercury | Hg | Technetium | Tc |
| Cesium | Cs | Molybdenum | Mo | **Tellurium** | **Te** |
| Chlorine | Cl | Neodymium | Nd | Terbium | Tb |
| Chromium | Cr | Neon | Ne | Thallium | Tl |
| Cobalt | Co | Neptunium | Np | Thorium | Th |
| **Copper** | **Cu** | Nickel | Ni | Thulium | Tm |
| Curium | Cm | Niobium | Nb | Tin | Sn |
| Dysprosium | Dy | Nitrogen | N | Titanium | Ti |
| Einsteinium | E | Nobelium | No | Tungsten | W |
| Erbium | Er | Osmium | Os | Uranium | U |
| Europium | Eu | Oxygen | O | Vanadium | V |
| Fermium | Fm | Palladium | Pd | Xenon | Xe |
| Fluorine | F | Phosphorus | P | Ytterbium | Yb |
| Francium | Fr | **Platinum** | **Pt** | Yttrium | Y |
| Gadolinium | Gd | Plutonium | Pu | Zinc | Zn |
| Gallium | Ga | Polonium | Po | Zirconium | Zr |
| Germanium | Ge | Potassium | K | | |
| **Gold** | **Au** | Praseodymium | Pr | | |

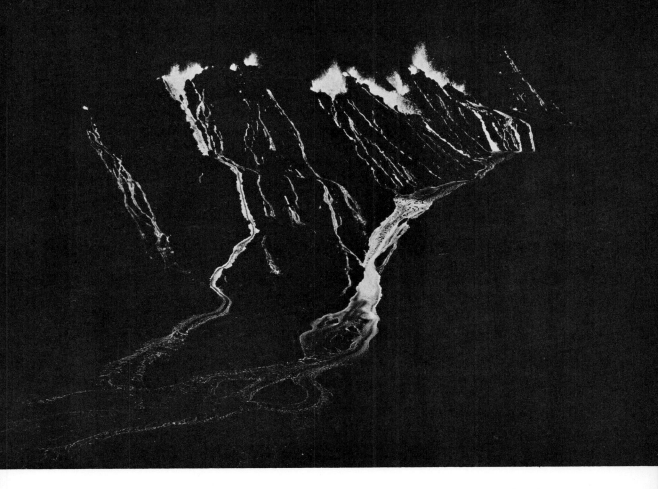

Molten rock spilling out of a Hawaiian volcano glows in the darkness as it floods the mountain slopes with slow-moving rivers of lava.

# 3 How Rocks Are Made

Rocks are all around us—in the walls of rushing streams, along cliff faces, on mountain sides; they are everywhere. If you took a rock apart and had a way of examining it closely, you would find that it is made up of bits and pieces of different kinds of minerals. In the previous chapter you found that elements such as silicon, oxygen, iron, potassium, and so on are the building blocks of minerals. In this chapter you will find that minerals are the building blocks of rocks.

To our eyes, during our short lifetime, the rocks of the Earth's crust seem ageless, yet they are always changing. They change as forces within the Earth squeeze the rock masses together and thrust them up as a new mountain range. Gradually the mountains are worn away by ice and water, which carry their bits and pieces onto the land below, or out to sea. Called **sediments**, the bits

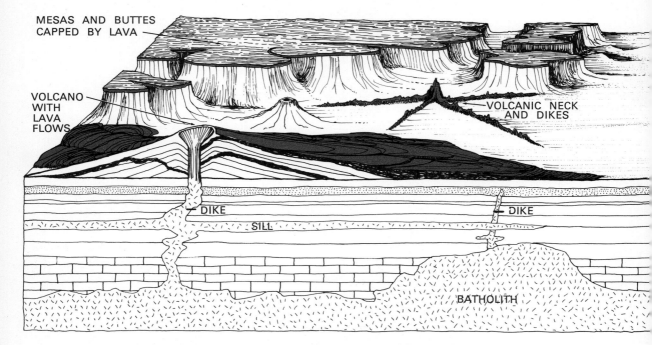

MESAS AND BUTTES
CAPPED BY LAVA

VOLCANO
WITH
LAVA
FLOWS

VOLCANIC NECK
AND DIKES

DIKE

DIKE

SILL

BATHOLITH

and pieces pile up and form layer upon layer—as spreading fans along the foothills of mountains, or on the shallow sea floor near the shore. Century after century the sediments continue to pile up, all the while being squeezed by the great weight of new sediments above. This squeezing process causes the sediments to harden into rock.

Just as the sediments are turned into rock, the rock, in turn, may be changed by forces within the Earth's crust. It may be melted, twisted, and folded, and gradually changed into a different kind of rock. This new rock may then be pushed up as a new mountain range and the process of wearing away begins anew.

### Igneous rock

If anyone asked you if you had ever watched a rock being formed, you probably would answer no. But possibly you have. If you have ever seen lava flowing out of a volcano, you have seen **igneous** rock being made. The word "igneous" comes from the Latin word *igneus,* meaning "fiery." Wherever a lava flow wells up out of a volcano and spills over the surrounding ground, we see convincing evidence that there is molten rock far below the surface of the Earth. This liquid rock is called **magma** before it flows out onto the Earth's surface. Magma is thought to exist in great pools within pockets of the solid crust, and possibly even within the mantle beneath the crust (see page 12).

As the diagram on this page shows, magma often seeps its way up through a crack or zone of weakness in the crust. Very often a large amount of magma hardens *before* it reaches the surface. On hardening underground, it forms a solid mass of igneous rock called a **batholith**. Batholiths may be hundreds of miles long and tens of miles wide. The Sierra Nevada Mountains along the

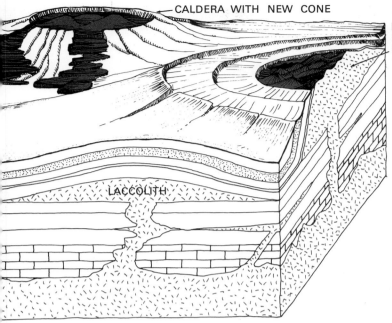

CALDERA WITH NEW CONE

LACCOLITH
EXPOSED
BY EROSION

LACCOLITH

## OCCURRENCE OF IGNEOUS ROCKS

Liquid rock called *magma* is thought to occupy great pockets within the solid rock of the Earth's crust. This diagram shows how magma seeps its way up through zones of weakness, forming solid masses of intrusive igneous rock, such as batholiths, laccoliths, dikes, and sills. It may also flow up to the surface, as lava.

California-Nevada border are an exposed batholith. They are about 400 miles long, 50 miles wide, and are more than 10,000 feet above sea level.

Sometimes the magma solidifies in such a way that it forms a dome-shaped mass which pushes up against the rock above, causing it to form a hill. When this happens, the igneous rock mass that forms is called a **laccolith. Dikes** are broad, flat masses of solidified magma that have flowed into vertical or nearly vertical cracks that may be many miles long. Very often the magma forces its way in between parallel layers of other rock and solidifies. When this happens, a **sill** is formed.

The batholiths, laccoliths, dikes, and sills form far below the Earth's surface. Because they do, they are said to be **intrusive** igneous rock formations. This term means that the magma has "intruded" into other rock, either forcing an opening for itself or by melting away parts of other rock. Since we cannot see intrusive igneous rocks forming, how do we know so much about them? Over the centuries rain, wind, and ice wear away the surface rocks and gradually expose the intrusive igneous rocks formed millions of years ago far below the surface. Such is the case of the Sierra Nevada Mountains and the famous ridge of igneous rock called the Palisades, lying along the Hudson River opposite New York City (see page 68). This sill, which formed about 190 million years ago, is now exposed for all to see.

Magma that does not solidify underground, but flows out of volcanoes and hardens on the Earth's surface is called **lava**. Lava deposits are called **extrusive** igneous rock. All igneous rock, then, is either intrusive or extrusive, depending on where it solidifies.

Another difference between intrusive and extrusive igneous rock is the size of the mineral grains which form when the magma or lava hardens. Magma usually cools and hardens at a very slow rate because magma is insulated by

29

Basalt, the dark rock at left, is extrusive igneous rock. Because it cools rapidly when it forms, it is made up of microscopic-size minerals. Granite pegmatite, the light-colored rock, cools slowly below the Earth's surface. As a result of the slow cooling, it has large mineral grains (outlined by colored circle).

surrounding rock and, therefore, loses its heat slowly. This slow cooling process produces large mineral grains. Each mineral in an intrusive igneous rock can be seen easily, even without a hand lens or magnifying glass. On rare occasions, single mineral crystals up to 45 feet or so long, and weighing as much as 90 tons, have been found. Granite, with its large mineral grains, is a common example of an intrusive igneous rock that has cooled slowly. Diorite, diabase, and gabbro are other examples (see table).

When lava cools and hardens, it does so quite quickly because it is exposed to the air. This fast cooling forms very small mineral grains, such as those found in the common extrusive igneous rock called basalt. Other common extrusive igneous rocks include felsite and andesite. They have barely recognizable minerals even when seen through a magnifying glass. Sometimes the cooling process may be so rapid that the individual atoms that make up the

Thick flows of basaltic lava emerging from a vent at about 2000° F often form a ropy surface as they solidify. They are known by the Hawaiian name *pahoehoe.*

materials of the rock do not have the chance to form fixed geometric patterns —hence, there are no minerals. Such is the case with volcanic glass called obsidian.

A table of some common igneous rocks is shown below. The left-hand column shows the various sizes of the mineral grains. Since it is only the silicate minerals that occur primarily in and classify igneous rocks, the chart also shows which kinds of silicate minerals are found in any igneous rock listed. For example, a rock that does not contain quartz but contains mostly the mafic minerals such as augite and hornblende, and some plagioclase feldspar, is called diabase *if the mineral grains are medium in size;* but if the mineral grains are fine, the rock is called basalt. The three igneous rocks shown in the heavy print are the most common ones. Finally, the place where the magma or lava cooled (either below the crust or on the surface) is shown in the right-hand column.

## SOME COMMON IGNEOUS ROCKS

| | SIZE OF MINERAL GRAINS | MINERAL COMPOSITION | | | | ORIGIN |
|---|---|---|---|---|---|---|
| | | *mostly felsic minerals and quartz* | *about half felsic and half mafic minerals (no quartz)* | *mostly mafic minerals and some plagioclase feldspar (no quartz)* | *only mafic minerals (no quartz or feldspar)* | |
| *minerals which can be seen by eye (coarse to medium texture)* | VERY LARGE *minerals are larger than ½", but of different sizes* | granite pegmatite | such rocks are rare | such rocks are rare | such rocks are rare | intrusive |
| | LARGE *minerals range from ⅛" to ½", but all minerals in a single rock are the same size* | **granite** | diorite | gabbro | peridotite or dunite | intrusive |
| | MEDIUM *minerals range from 1/16" to ⅛", but all minerals in a single rock are the same size* | **granite** | diorite | diabase | peridotite or dunite | intrusive |
| *minerals which cannot be seen easily without magnification (fine to very fine texture)* | FINE TO MICROSCOPIC *minerals are smaller than 1/16", all are the same size* | felsite | **andesite** | **basalt** | such rocks are rare | extrusive |
| | *porous glassy-appearing* | obsidian | pumice | scoria | such rocks are rare | extrusive |

RIVER CARRYING SEDIMENTS

GRANITIC ROCK OF CONTINENT

CONTINENTAL SHELF

OCEAN

CONTINENTAL SLOPE

BASALTIC ROCK BENEATH OCEAN AND CONTINENT

Rivers flowing over the land carry sand, gravel, clay, and other sediments down to the sea. Eventually they are dumped onto the continental shelf and are carried by the currents out toward the continental slope. Sometimes they pile up on the edge of the shelf, then break away and tumble down the slope and out onto the deep-sea floor. Meanwhile, marine organisms living in the warm waters above the shelf die, sink to the bottom, and become part of the sediments.

### Sedimentary rock

About three-quarters of the rock exposed at the Earth's surface is sedimentary rock. Yet if we were able to drill down into the crust to a depth of about 10 miles, only 5 per cent or so of the material drilled through would be sedimentary rock. The sedimentary rock record is written entirely on the surface of the Earth. Sedimentary rocks are made of bits and pieces of other kinds of rock, and often contain the remains of once-living things. Blackboard chalk is sedimentary rock containing microscopic shells of sea animals that died and sank to the ocean bottom millions of years ago.

Every time you walk through the sand at a beach, or step into the ooze on a lake bottom, or over the pebbles, gravel, or clay of a stream bed, you are walking on materials that millions of years from now may turn into sedimentary rock. Did you ever wonder where the sediment materials—mud, lime, sand, and clay—come from? As soft as they may be to touch, they were once part of solid rock. The rocks of mountains are cracked by frost and worn away by wind and water. Small pieces of rocks are always being broken off and carried by a mountain stream or river flowing toward the sea. Certain sections of the stream bed itself may be bedrock that is constantly being worn away by water. Or as a river scours its bed and erodes its banks, mud, clay, and other materials are swept along toward the sea. All of the bits and pieces of material are called **sediments**. The word "sedimentary" comes from the Latin word *sedimentum*, meaning "settling."

Around the base of the Rockies and Adirondacks, the layers of sediments are only paper thin compared with the thickness of sediments elsewhere on our planet. The Mississippi River has been dumping sediments into the Gulf of Mexico for more than 500,000 years. As a result, the sediments it has deposited are more than 20,000 feet thick. Sedimentary material brought down to the sea by the River Ganges in India are thought to be about 50,000 feet thick.

32

The sediments tend to build up in layers. For centuries a river may carry fine particles of clay down to the sea. Gradually the clay particles settle to the bottom of a bay. Then for some reason the river may speed up its flow and so be able to carry much heavier particles, such as sand, over a greater distance. Now particles of sand are laid down on top of the clay. The bay also may go through a period of rich marine life; over many, many years the marine creatures die and their remains settle to the bottom forming a third layer of sediments. And so the process continues. You can see this layering, or **bedding,** as it is called, when you examine sedimentary rocks in a quarry wall or

This bluff in Wyoming, eroded away by weather over the centuries, clearly shows bedding, or the layering of various types of sediments turned to rock.

cliff face. Each layer of sedimentary rock usually is of a slightly different color from the one above and below it. Anyone who has seen the famous Painted Desert in Arizona can appreciate the wide color range of sedimentary rocks.

One question we have not yet answered is how the soft sediments turn into hard rock, or become **lithified**, as the geologist says. There are three ways:

1   The gravels on a river bottom, or the fine sands on parts of the ocean floor, are made up of billions upon billions of individual particles. Over a long period of time this mass of particles is cemented together by minerals, which act as glue-like substances. Some of the minerals contained in the water bathing the sediments include hematite, quartz, and calcite. Geologists do not know what makes the mineral "glue" go to work as a cementing agent, but it does. If sediments are made up of sand, the sedimentary rock produced is **sandstone.** If the sediments are made up of gravel mixed with other materials, the sedimentary rock formed is **conglomerate.** This cementing process of making sedimentary rocks is called **cementation.**

2   What if the sediments particles are so small—clay particles, say—and so tightly packed that water cannot move among them freely? This often happens to layers of clay and silt. Over the years a layer of clay 50 feet thick may be laid down. If heavy layers of other materials are deposited on top, the clay may be compacted, or squeezed, to a thickness of only 25 feet. Eventually the clay will be squeezed into hard rock which is then called shale. Deposits of sand and gravel also can become compacted. But because sand

When coarse sediments made up of gravel are mixed with other materials, a rock called *conglomerate* is formed. Jackknife shows size.

and gravel grains are much larger than clay and silt particles, sand and gravel do not compact as well.

If compaction takes place on the sea floor, the great weight of the overlying material may squeeze water out of the material being compacted. Or, if the sea dries up, the water in the material being compacted slowly evaporates. This loss of water through squeezing or through evaporation is called **desiccation**. By the time most of the water has left the sedimentary material being compacted, the sediments have turned to hard rock.

3 Have you ever "grown" a crystal garden? Certain minerals contained in sediment deposits, particularly in fine mud, react with each other in such a way that crystals, such as quartz, are formed. Geologists do not understand exactly how crystallization takes place in sedimentary material, but they do know that crystal forming is one of the processes that changes some of the soft sedimentary material into hard rock.

The table below lists several sedimentary rocks and shows the sedimentary materials that form them.

## SOME COMMON SEDIMENTARY ROCKS

| NAME OF ROCK | MADE OF (SEDIMENT) | ORIGIN |
|---|---|---|
| **mudstone** and **shale** | clay and silt (the mineral kaolin) | DETRITAL (mineral and rock remains of broken-down rock. "Detrital" means "worn down") |
| **sandstone** | sand (particles of the mineral quartz or particles of other minerals or rocks) | |
| **conglomerate** (called "breccia," if the lithified gravel has lots of angular fragments) | pebbles, gravel (large particles of any kind of rock or mineral) | |
| **gypsum rock** | gypsum | non-living materials |
| **rock salt** | halite | CHEMICAL (minerals formed as a result of chemical precipitation) |
| **limestone** | calcite | |
| **dolomitic limestone** | dolomite, calcite | |
| **limestone, chalk** | (pieces of microscopic shells) | ORGANIC (made up of the remains of once-living things) |
| **coal** | plant remains | |

### Metamorphic rock

As you found out earlier in this chapter, and in the first chapter, deep within the Earth's crust rock is under great pressure and is very hot. The pressure and heat are caused, in part, by the great weight of the many miles of rock pressing down from above. It is in this deep zone of the crust that we find igneous and sedimentary rock undergoing many changes, changes that produce that class of rock called **metamorphic** rock (meaning "change of form").

The heat and pressure deep within the crust are so great that the rock there is not solid in the same way that rocks on the Earth's surface are solid. Like soft putty, rock deep within the crust can be bent, folded, squeezed, and stretched into any shape. Any kind of hard rock—igneous, sedimentary, or metamorphic—from six to seven or so miles beneath the Earth's surface is thought to be under pressures of from 40,000 to 60,000 pounds per square inch, and at temperatures of about 1500° F.

In general, there are two ways in which metamorphic rock is formed. One way is called **regional metamorphism**. The rocks that are now the Rocky Mountains and the Appalachian Mountains long, long ago were vast flat collections of sediments many thousands of feet deep. As new sediments continued to be deposited on top, the older ones beneath were being squeezed. Those at the deepest levels were being squeezed the most. Near the top, then, clay, sand, and other materials were gradually changing into sedimentary rock by compaction. Deeper down, in the older sediment beds, rock of sedimentary material had already been formed. And much deeper, the still older sedimentary rock was being changed to metamorphic rock by heat and pressure. The forces were so great that the layers of rock were bent, folded, and crumpled.

These great pressures and high temperatures within the Earth that crumple rock like paper change the very substance of the original rock. By some complicated process still not well understood, new minerals are formed out of old ones as the metamorphic rocks are forming. These new mineral grains tend to be large enough to be seen without a magnifying glass or hand lens. If the new minerals are flat, like biotite or muscovite mica, or long and slender, such as the mineral hornblende, they are often arranged in almost parallel "layers." The "layering" of such minerals in a metamorphic rock is called **foliation**. To a beginning rock and mineral collector, the layering of the visible minerals in a metamorphic rock resembles the bedding of sedimentary rocks. A good rule-of-thumb to help you distinguish between metamorphic and sedimentary rocks is that the minerals that make up most of the regional metamorphic rocks can be seen very easily without magnification. But in most sedimentary rocks the minerals or pieces of other rocks that make up the sedimentary rock usually cannot be seen, even when you look at them with a hand lens.

**Contact metamorphism** is another way in which metamorphic rock is formed. Earlier you saw that igneous intrusions of magma sometimes force their way into the surrounding rock and form batholiths, dikes, and sills. Where the hot magma comes in contact with the surrounding solid rock, metamorphic rock is formed. The width of these zones of contact metamorphic rock depends upon the size of the intrusion. Batholiths form thick contact metamorphic zones, maybe hundreds of feet wide. But a thin dike or sill forms a contact metamorphic zone only fractions of a foot wide. The high temperature of the magma in contact with the surrounding rock forms new minerals in the contact metamorphic zone. It is in these zones that some of the most interesting minerals can be found and, very often, mines and quarries are located there.

In contact metamorphism, then, heat is the main cause of change; in regional metamorphism, heat and pressure together cause igneous, sedimentary, and older metamorphic rocks to change into new metamorphic rocks. But in neither case is the heat and pressure great enough to melt the original rock. If this should happen, magma would form. When it hardened, an intrusive igneous rock would come into being. Some common metamorphic rocks are listed in the table on page 38.

The heat of the magma contact metamorphosed the limestone into light-colored marble adjacent to the black sill (colored arrow) in Glacier National Park, Montana (left). When pressure changes rock deep within the crust, such regional metamorphic rock as those examined by author Schuberth on Mt. Washington are foliated and much deformed.

We have seen that the rock making up the Earth's crust is constantly changing, but the processes that form and change them are so slow that we rarely see them taking place. The many different kinds of rocks tell us fascinating stories of the everchanging Earth, each rock telling a story in its own way. Let us now find out how to identify rocks and minerals. We will do so not only by looking at them, but also by making some very simple tests.

## SOME COMMON METAMORPHIC ROCKS

| KIND OF METAMORPHISM | NAME OF ROCK | CHIEF MINERALS | ROCK IS MADE FROM | STRUCTURE OF ROCK | SIZE OF MINERALS |
|---|---|---|---|---|---|
| regional | slate | muscovite kaolin | clay rock (shale, for example) | foliated (called slaty cleavage) | microscopic |
| regional | phyllite | muscovite feldspar quartz | clay rock (slightly coarser than clay rock of slate) | foliated | barely seen without 10-power magnification |
| regional | mica schist* (hornblende schist) | muscovite, biotite (hornblende) feldspar, quartz | mostly clay rock | foliated | easily seen without magnification |
| regional | gneiss* (pronounced like "nice") | mica, feldspar, quartz | granite, sandstones, and others | foliated | easily seen without magnification |
| regional and contact | marble | calcite and dolomite | metamorphosed limestone and dolomite | foliated | usually easily seen without magnification |
| contact | hornfels (baked shale) | mica, kaolin | clay rock | not foliated | microscopic |
| regional and contact | quartzite | quartz | quartz sandstone and conglomerate | not foliated | barely seen without magnification |

*Although the minerals may be the same in a schist and gneiss, the gneiss usually appears as a rock with bands of minerals, each band being about ½ inch or so thick.

Granite pegmatite, intrusive igneous rock with thick books of mica.

# 4 Identifying Minerals and Rocks

When you begin to collect minerals and rocks you will be surprised to discover how much they differ in color, weight, hardness, coarseness or fineness of texture, and shape. These differences depend on what each specimen is made of and how it was formed. In this chapter you will learn how to go about identifying a mineral. Once you can identify a mineral, learning to identify a rock becomes a much simpler task.

As you saw in Chapter 3, a rock is a mixture of minerals, the fragments of minerals or other rocks. It often contains once-living organisms, or it may consist entirely of them. The Earth's crust is made up of three basic types of rocks. Depending on how a particular rock was formed, it is igneous, sedimentary, or metamorphic. Before you go rock hunting, read Chapter 5 to find out which types of rocks you are likely to find in the area you are most interested in visiting.

### Telling rocks from minerals

One of the problems of a beginning rock collector is knowing whether a specimen is a rock, or a large piece of a single mineral. For example, basalt is an igneous rock usually composed of three minerals (augite, hornblende, and plagioclase feldspar). But these minerals are so dark and so finely mixed together that you can't see the minerals separately, not even under a hand lens. So basalt rock appears uniformly dark gray to black and appears quite dense, just as if it were a single mineral.

While basalt (below) is made up of three different minerals, the rock looks so uniform that it may be taken for a mineral. The sandstone (top) and marble (bottom, right) are good examples of *mono-minerallic* rocks, or rocks made up of many individual pieces of a single mineral (quartz in sandstone, and calcite in marble). Notice the shiny cleavage surface of the calcite in the marble.

Some rocks are composed almost entirely of many pieces of the same mineral. For example, sandstone is a sedimentary rock composed almost entirely of many pieces of quartz. Another example is marble, a metamorphic rock composed almost entirely of many individual pieces of the mineral calcite.

How, then, can you distinguish a single specimen of a mineral from rocks such as basalt, sandstone, or marble? Fortunately, minerals have distinctive properties that set them apart from rocks, and apart from each other. With experience and much patience you will soon learn to distinguish between minerals and the common rocks.

The specimen of granite pegmatite (top left) shows that the rock is made up of a mixture of different minerals—orthoclase feldspar (top right), quartz (bottom left), and mica (bottom right).

How to make a scratch test:

With the window glass lying flat, press down very hard with the mineral (quartz crystals are shown here) and make a scratch. Then, with your finger, try to rub away the mark. In this case a deep scratch remains. So the quartz is much harder than 5½ — the hardness of the glass plate. Minerals softer than 5½ on Mohs scale do not scratch glass.

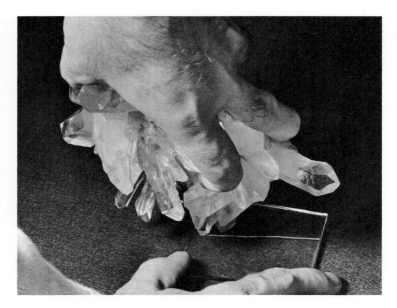

## Clues to a mineral's identity

To identify a mineral specimen, or minerals in a rock specimen that are large enough to see, first make some simple observations and tests. Here are seven things to look for and test:

1 HARDNESS  One of the most dependable physical properties of a mineral is its hardness—which means how easily it can be scratched, or abraded. If you scratch two minerals together, the harder one will always leave a scratch on the softer one. By scratching your specimen with different minerals of known hardness—or with common things such as your fingernail, a knife blade, or a piece of thick window glass—you can find the **relative hardness** of the mineral you want to identify. Or, you can use the mineral you want to identify to scratch a mineral of known hardness. When doing this, always use a sharp edge of the mineral you are testing against a smooth surface of the mineral of known hardness, or common object such as glass.

One of the softest minerals found in nature is talc; the hardest is diamond. Relative hardness is measured by a scale drawn up more than a hundred years ago by the German mineralogist Friedrich Mohs and which is still in use. He numbered 10 minerals in the order of their hardness, from talc (No. 1) to diamond (No. 10).

### MOHS SCALE OF RELATIVE HARDNESS

| 1 | Talc | 6 | Feldspar |
|---|------|---|----------|
| 2 | Gypsum | 7 | Quartz |
| 3 | Calcite | 8 | Topaz |
| 4 | Fluorite | 9 | Corundum |
| 5 | Apatite | 10 | Diamond |

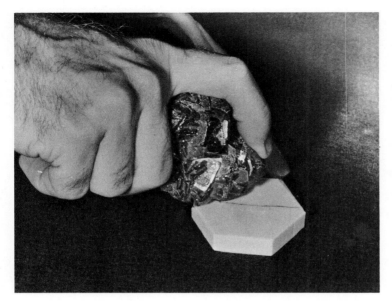

How to make a streak test:

Press down and streak the mineral across an unglazed, porcelain tile held flat. The color of the powdered trail left behind is the streak of the mineral. Minerals harder than 7, the hardness of the tile plate, scratch the tile plate instead of leaving a powdered streak.

On this scale, the hardness of your fingernail is a little over 2; a copper penny is about 3; a steel pocketknife blade, or ordinary window glass, is about 5½; a tempered-steel file is about 6½; unglazed porcelain tile is about 7. You can make the scratch test with these materials, or you can buy a hardness set of the first nine minerals in the Mohs scale from a mineral supply store for about two dollars. If, for example, calcite does not scratch your specimen, but fluorite does, then you know that the hardness of the unknown mineral is between 3 and 4, possibly 3½. Be sure to rub your finger over what may only appear to be a scratch. If it is just a powder trail, the powder will easily rub off and there will not be a scratch.

If you use a glass plate, make sure that it lies firmly on a flat surface. Press hard with a sharp edge of the mineral you are testing to see if it scratches the glass plate. Then carefully rub away the powder that will always form. If the mineral is softer than the glass plate, it will not leave a scratch on the glass. But if the mineral is harder than the glass plate, notice how deep the scratch is on the glass plate. The deeper the scratch, the harder the mineral is.

Notice that the "Mineral Identification Key" on page 50 is arranged so that the first property of the mineral you should determine is its hardness. Perform the hardness test very carefully, otherwise you may be misled in identifying your mineral.

2 COLOR    The color of a mineral can be the mineral's most obvious physical property. But it is one of the *least* reliable ways to identify a mineral. A single mineral may vary widely in color from one specimen to another. Only a few minerals, such as galena, hornblende, and graphite, are uniform in color.

3 STREAK    Much more reliable than the color of a mineral is the color of its streak. The streak is the color of the powdered mineral. To get a streak, scratch your specimen against a piece of common, unglazed porcelain tile. Even the edge of a thick porcelain dish will do—but make sure you scratch a *broken* edge, not the smooth, glazed surface. If the mineral is softer than the

43

The dull, waxy luster of quartz chalcedony (left) differs from the bright, metallic luster of the mineral galena.

porcelain, it will leave a thin, colored streak of powder. The color of the streak is often different from the color of the mineral specimen itself. But the streak of color left is usually the same from one specimen to another of the same mineral, even though the colors of the same mineral may differ. For example, fluorite is found in many different colors, but the color of the streak is always white.

4 LUSTER    Like color, luster, which also depends on light, is another physical property of minerals. What kind of "shine" does the mineral have when light is reflected from its surface? Two different minerals with the same color may have different luster because of the way light is reflected from them. Does one shine like metal and so have a metallic luster? Does the other appear pearly, waxy, greasy, glassy, or silky? These are some of the common terms used to describe a mineral's luster.

5 HEFT    Heft or, more accurately, **specific gravity,** refers to the density or amount of matter contained in a given volume of a substance compared to the same volume of water. A mineral five times as dense as water, for example, has a specific gravity of 5. Gold has a specific gravity of 19.3, galena 7.5, and quartz 2.7. You will not be able to find out accurately the specific gravity of a mineral. A special technique and special instruments are required to do this. But by "hefting" a specimen you can tell if it is unusually heavy or light. The heavier it feels, the higher its specific gravity.

6 MINERAL BREAKAGE    If you have a broken piece of the mineral you want to identify, carefully study the way the mineral has broken. A mineral can break in one of two ways.

A mineral can **fracture** irregularly instead of breaking along smooth, parallel surfaces. The surfaces of a mineral that does fracture are quite rough and very irregular in shape. But some minerals (and even a rock such as obsidian) fracture with some of their surfaces strikingly curved. This shell-like

Some minerals like quartz (right) fracture irregularly when they are broken. The rock obsidian (left) shows a conchoidal fracture; it breaks along smooth, curved surfaces like the inside surface of a shell.

fracture is called a **conchoidal** fracture. (The word "conchoidal" comes from the Greek words *konche,* meaning "shell," and *eidos,* meaning "form.") Frequently, these curved, shell-like surfaces have almost razor-sharp edges and corners. In flaking flint or other similar materials, prehistoric men made good use of this sharp-edged property of conchoidal fracture.

A mineral can also **cleave**. Cleavage is the capacity of a mineral for breaking apart along certain planes. Cleavage leaves flat and fairly smooth parallel surfaces on the mineral. For example, mica cleaves (splits) easily into leaves, or flat sheets, that are parallel. Since the mineral cleaves in only one direction (and fractures along the other directions), mica is said to have a **one-directional cleavage**.

When a mineral has **two-directional cleavage**, parallel surfaces occur in two different directions. For example, the feldspar minerals have a two-directional cleavage. They split along two different surfaces that meet nearly at right angles.

Galena has a **three-directional cleavage**. Each of the three directions (the three cleavage surfaces) meet at right angles. So you must first see how many

These photographs show one-directional cleavage in mica (left), two-directional in feldspar (center), and three-directional in halite.

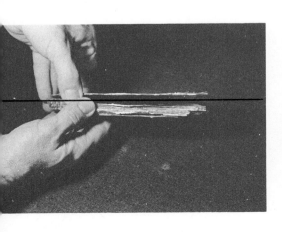
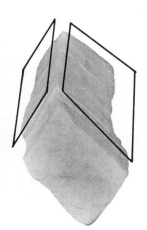
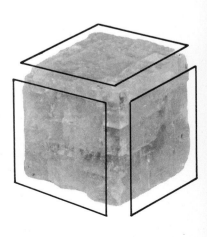

directions of cleavage a mineral has. Then, if it has more than one direction, you must see at what angle the planes meet. Quite simply, it is either a right angle, or it is not a right angle.

Cleavage is perhaps the most difficult physical property to master in identifying a mineral. It might help if you remember that most minerals usually have no more than two directions of cleavage. A few have only one or three directions, and some minerals do not have cleavage at all. They fracture entirely. The cleavage surfaces of a mineral with two directions can usually be recognized by their shinier luster when compared to the duller luster of the fracture surfaces of the same specimen.

7 OTHER PROPERTIES   In addition to the physical properties just described, some minerals have other useful identifying properties. For instance, some are attracted by a magnet, such as magnetite, but most are not. Other minerals **fluoresce**, or glow in various brilliant colors when they are held under ultraviolet light. Willemite and some types of calcite are examples. Still other minerals, such as albite and labradorite, are characterized by fine, parallel scratches or striations that naturally occur on certain cleavage surfaces; or minerals such as labradorite and precious opal (not technically a mineral because its atoms are not fixed in a definite geometric pattern) show an internal display of brilliant patches of color. Although minerals differ in still other ways, the main physical properties just described are more than adequate to enable you to identify the more common minerals.

If the mineral you are trying to identify is not one of the 26 listed in the "Mineral Identification Key" on page 50, you can discover what it is by checking your findings against mineral descriptions in one of the books listed on page 119.

To organize your findings of the physical properties of your unidentified minerals, use the "Mineral Identification Worksheet." First fill in the columns

The mineral labradorite feldspar shows distinct but faint parallel striations on its cleavage surface. (Colored lines show striations.)

46

and then turn to the "Mineral Identification Key" to identify your mineral if it is one of the 26 listed. Make your own additional worksheets by copying the one shown. Can you identify the five minerals whose physical properties are described for you as a guide? (They are included in the "Mineral Identification Key.") With practice, you soon will be able to identify any one of the common minerals by finding only two or, at the most, three of its physical properties.

## Mineral Identification Worksheet

| NAME OF MINERAL | HARDNESS | COLOR | STREAK | BREAKAGE | LUSTER | OTHER PROPERTIES |
|---|---|---|---|---|---|---|
| | Less than 2½ | colorless to yellowish-white | White | Perfect cleavage in one direction | Pearly | Easily splits apart into very thin, transparent sheets. Thin sheets of the mineral bend and then return to their original position. Looks like cellophane. |
| | 4 | brassy to golden-yellow | Black | Fracture | Metallic | Feels rather heavy when hefted |
| | 7 | Variable | White | Conchoidal Fracture | Waxy | Sharp corners and edges |
| | 3 | White | White | 3 cleavage directions none of which are at 90° to each other | Pearly | |
| | 7 | white | white | Fracture | Glassy | |

## What kind of rock is it?

To identify a rock, you do not have to test it as you do a mineral. In the first place, there are only a few different kinds of rocks in the Earth's crust compared to the many minerals. This greatly reduces the number of possibilities for the kind of rock specimen you have. Also, most rocks can be identified just by carefully looking at them. But there are certain things you should keep in mind when you study a rock specimen.

First, you should find out what kind of **texture** it has. By texture we mean the size of the minerals or other rock fragments that make up the rock. If you can clearly see the minerals without a hand lens, you can say that the texture is *coarse* to *medium*. (See the sample of granite pegmatite on page 41.) If you can see the minerals only by using a hand lens, consider the texture as *fine*. If you don't see any minerals at all, even with a hand lens, the texture is *very fine*. But remember that this is a very simple classification of texture.

In addition to finding out what kind of texture a rock has, you should also find out what kind or kinds of minerals it contains. For rocks with a coarse or medium texture, this should not be too difficult. But for rocks with a fine or very fine texture, you may have to depend on the hardness of the rock or even its general color.

Finally, you should try to see if the rock splits along definite planes of weakness. Sedimentary rocks such as shale, sandstone, and some limestones, as well as some metamorphic rocks such as slate, usually split along planes of weakness quite easily. On the other hand, other metamorphic rocks show clearly defined layers of one of the minerals (called "foliation," see Chapter 3) that make up the rock. For example, the layering of mica or hornblende in a schist or gneiss is a striking feature in these rocks.

You should always study the fresh, unweathered surface of the rock you are trying to identify. The surface exposed to the atmosphere usually looks

Layering, or stratification, is clearly visible in this sample of sedimentary rock, which splits (bottom photograph) along definite planes of weakness.

completely different from the unweathered rock underneath—just as tarnished silver looks quite different from fresh, unweathered silver. To get a fresh surface, all you have to do is split the rock in half. But always do this at the collecting site, not at home. Otherwise you may end up with a specimen too small for your collection. When you want to identify a rock, carefully follow the "Rock Identification Key" step by step. You should have little difficulty in keying out your rock specimen if it is one of the 18 rocks listed. Again, if your specimen does not fit one of the descriptions given in the key, you may find it in one of the books listed on page 119.

Wavy dark layers of biotite and light layers of quartz and feldspar in this gneiss from New York City show how pressure formed this metamorphic rock.

# HOW TO IDENTIFY 26 COMMON MINERALS

## A Mineral Identification Key

Use this key to identify a specimen of a single mineral, or to identify individual bits of a mineral in a rock. First find the hardness, cleavage, color, color of the streak, and luster of the mineral, as explained in this chapter. From your findings, answer the question on line **A.** Your "yes" or "no" answer will guide you to the next question to answer. By moving step by step through the key as directed, you can identify the mineral, *if it is one of the 26 listed.*

After you have identified your mineral, you might want to read a complete description of it in one of the rock and mineral books listed on page 119.

Many of the minerals you find will not be included here, so you will not be able to key them out. If this is the case, check your findings of the physical properties with the mineral descriptions in one of the reference books.

**A** Is the specimen's hardness less than 2½? (Can you scratch it with your fingernail?) If yes, see line **1**, below. If not, see line **B.**

**1** Is cleavage perfect in one direction? If yes, see lines **a, b,** and **c,** below. If not, see line **2.**

    **a** If thin sheets are transparent, if thicker pieces are colorless or light in color, and if the cleavage surfaces are very shiny, the mineral is...............................MUSCOVITE MICA

    **b** If the description above applies, except that the color is dark brown to black, the mineral is ................................................................................................BIOTITE MICA

    **c** If there is a second cleavage direction, and if a silky to satiny luster is evident, the mineral is ....................................................................................................GYPSUM

**2** If there is no definite cleavage, see lines **a, b,** and **c,** below.

    **a** If the mineral is mostly white, with a dull luster, and has an earthy odor when moistened, it is ...............................................................................................KAOLIN

    **b** If the mineral is mostly white or greenish white, with a silky luster, and feels slippery to the touch, it is ...........................................................................................TALC

    **c** If the mineral is mostly black, with a metallic luster, and feels slippery to the touch, it is ...............................................................................................................GRAPHITE

**B** Is the hardness more than 2½ but less than 5½? (Is it too hard to be scratched by a fingernail, but will not scratch glass?) If yes, see line **1**, below. If not, see line **C.**

**1** Is cleavage three-directional? If yes, see line **a,** below. If not, see line **2.**

    **a** Do all cleavage surfaces join at right angles? If yes, see lines **1** and **2,** below. If not, see line **b.**

        **1** If the mineral is black, with a metallic luster, and shows a black streak, it is....GALENA

        **2** If the mineral is light in color, and tastes salty, it is.......................................HALITE

    **b** If the cleavage surfaces fail to meet at right angles, and if the mineral is mostly white or milky white in color with a pearly luster, it is...............................................CALCITE

**2** Is the cleavage generally two-directional? If yes, see line **a,** below. If not, see line **3.**

    **a** If the two cleavage surfaces are at acute angles, if the mineral appears translucent to transparent, and if it shows a rather glassy luster, it is.................................FLUORITE

**3** If there is no definite cleavage, see line **a,** below.

    **a** Is the luster metallic? If yes, see lines **1** and **2** below. If not, see line **b.**

**1** If the mineral has a brownish red streak, it is........................................HEMATITE

**2** If the mineral is yellow, has a brassy luster, and leaves a black streak, it is

CHALCOPYRITE

**b** Is the luster dull? If yes, see line **1** below.

**1** If the mineral has a rusty yellow to pale orange streak, it is....................LIMONITE

**C** Is the hardness more than 5½, but less than 7? (Will the mineral scratch glass, but not unglazed porcelain tile?) If yes, see line **1**, below. If not, see line **D**.

**1** When you press a sharp edge of the mineral against the glass, does it leave only a *faint* scratch? If yes, see line **a**, below. If not, see line **2**.

**a** Is cleavage two-directional? If yes, see line **1**, below. If not, see line **b**.

**1** Do the cleavage surfaces join at right angles? If yes, see lines **A**, **B**, **C**, and **D**, below. If not, see line **2**.

**A** If the mineral is salmon pink or tuna-fish pink, it is...........ORTHOCLASE FELDSPAR

**B** If the mineral is white or gray, and contains very faint parallel striations on a well-developed cleavage surface, it is....................ALBITE FELDSPAR

**C** If the mineral is dark gray, contains very faint parallel striations on a well-developed cleavage surface, and shows an internal peacock blue and iridescent blue-green play of color, it is...........LABRADORITE FELDSPAR

**D** If the mineral is dark green to black, it is.................AUGITE

**2** If the two cleavage surfaces do not meet at right angles, and the color is dark green to black, the mineral is.......................HORNBLENDE

**b** If there is no definite cleavage, see line **1**, below.

**1** Is the luster metallic? If yes, see lines **A** and **B**, below.

**A** If the mineral is yellow, and leaves a black streak, it is...........PYRITE

**B** If the mineral is black, leaves a black streak, and is quite dense, and may be magnetic, it is...........MAGNETITE

**2** When you press a sharp edge of the mineral against glass, does it leave a *deep* scratch? If yes, see line **a**, below.

**a** Is the luster glassy, rather than metallic? If yes, see lines **1**, **2**, and **3**, below. If not, see line **b**.

**1** If the mineral is deep wine-red in color, it is.......................GARNET

**2** If the mineral is colorless, milky, or smoky, it is.......................QUARTZ

**3** If the mineral shows a granular texture, and is rather olive green, it is...........OLIVINE

**b** Is the luster dull and rather waxy? If yes, see line **1**, below.

**1** If the mineral shows a distinct conchoidal fracture which leaves smooth curved surfaces that have sharp edges and corners, it is...........QUARTZ CHALCEDONY

**D** Is the hardness greater than 7? (Does the mineral leave a deep scratch on the glass and a faint scratch on the porcelain tile plate?) If yes, see lines **1** and **2**, below.

**1** If the mineral is commonly black, green, or pink in color, with a glassy luster, and the long crystals show numerous fine grooves running parallel to each other for the length of the crystal faces, it is.......................TOURMALINE

**2** If the mineral is generally greenish blue, pale yellowish, or yellowish green, or pale pink to lilac in color, and shows an irregular to conchoidal fracture with a glassy luster, it is...........BERYL

# HOW TO IDENTIFY 18 COMMON ROCKS

## A Rock Identification Key

Use this key to identify a specimen of rock. Make certain that you always study the fresh and unweathered surface. A surface long exposed to the weather very often looks entirely different from a fresh and unweathered surface. If you can see individual minerals in the rock sample, always identify them first. Then find the answer to the question on line **A** by examining your specimen. Your "yes" or "no" answer will guide you to the next question to answer. A look at your specimen should enable you to answer each of these questions, and your answers will lead you to the name of the rock, *if it is one of the 18 listed here.* After you have identified your rock specimen, you might want to read a complete description of it in one of the rock and mineral books listed on page 119.

Some of the rocks you find will not be included here, so you will not be able to key them out. If this is the case, check your findings of the physical characteristics with rock descriptions in one of the reference books.

**A** Can you see individual minerals or particles of rock that make up the specimen, without using a magnifying lens? If yes, see line **1,** below. If not, see line **B.**

**1** Are the minerals distributed at random, or not in any definite pattern? Are the minerals tightly locked together, making the rock rather hard to split? If yes, see line **a,** below. If no, see line **2.**

    **a** Are the minerals light-colored, largely quartz, feldspar, and mica? If yes, see lines **1** and **2,** below. If no, see line **b.**

    **1** If the mineral particles are less than ¼ inch in size, but all are about the same size, the rock is ............................................................................................ **GRANITE**

    **2** If the mineral particles vary greatly in size, and many are larger than ¼ inch, the rock is ........................................................................ **GRANITE PEGMATITE**

    **b** Is the mineral interlocking calcite, which will not scratch glass? If not, see line **c,** below. If yes, the rock is ............................................................. **MARBLE**

    **c** Are the minerals mainly dark-colored (augite, hornblende, and feldspar), all about the same size, and the rock generally dark-colored? If no, see line **d,** below. If yes, the rock is probably ................................................................. **GABBRO**

    **d** Are the dark-colored minerals, such as augite and hornblende, in about equal amount to the light-colored minerals, such as feldspar? If yes, the rock is probably ....... **DIORITE**

**2** Are the minerals arranged in planes, or bands, which you can see, and which tend to make the rock split along these planes? If yes, see lines **a** and **b,** below. If not, see line **3.**

    **a** If the planes of aligned minerals are quite thin, the rock is ............................ **SCHIST**

    **b** If the planes of aligned minerals appear as broad and thick bands of alternating layers of light- and dark-colored minerals (such as quartz and feldspar in the light layers, and biotite mica and hornblende in the dark layers), the rock is ............................ **GNEISS**

**3** Is the specimen composed of rounded particles of minerals or other rocks? If yes, see lines **a** and **b,** below.

**a** If the particles are large, rounded pebbles, the rock is ..................... CONGLOMERATE

**b** If the particles are sand-sized grains of mostly quartz, which will scratch glass, the rock is ................................................................... SANDSTONE

**B** Can you barely see the particles of minerals or rock, even when using a magnifying lens? If yes, see line **1**, below. If not, see line **2**.

**1** The minerals would be distributed at random or not in any definite pattern if you could easily see them. If they are tightly locked together, making the rock hard to split, see lines **a**, **b**, **c**, and **d**, below. If not, see line **2**.

**a** If the minerals are dark-colored, such as augite, hornblende, and feldspar, and the rock is dark gray to black in color (but often shows a yellow to reddish orange weathered outside surface), and will usually scratch glass, the rock is ................................ BASALT

**b** The same description as in item **a** directly above, except that if the rock contains many holes, or vesicles, it is ................................................................ SCORIA

**c** If the minerals are light-colored, such as quartz and feldspar, and the rock is a pale pink to reddish in color, the rock is .......................................................... FELSITE

**d** If the mineral is largely light-colored quartz that is fused together, and will scratch glass, the rock is ................................................................................ QUARTZITE

**2** If the individual particles of the rock cannot be seen under a magnifying lens, but if the rock appears to be layered, and is too soft to scratch glass, see line **a**, below. If not, see line **C**.

**a** Does the rock split easily into layers? If yes, see lines **1** and **2**, below. If not, see line **b**.

**1** If the luster on the split surface is dull, the rock is ................................... SHALE

**2** If the luster on the split surface seems silky, the rock is ............................. SLATE

**b** If the rock is largely composed of calcite (and, therefore, may not scratch glass), and if the rock does not split easily into layers, it is probably ............................... LIMESTONE

**C** If you cannot see any minerals, even with a 10-power magnifying lens, see lines **1**, **2**, and **3**, below.

**1** If the rock is dark-colored (but often shows a yellow to reddish orange or brown weathered outside surface), and if it contains many holes, or vesicles, the rock is .......... SCORIA

**2** If the rock is light-colored and contains many holes or vesicles (little air spaces that in some cases enable the rock to float on the surface of fresh water), the rock is ....... PUMICE

**3** If the rock is jet black, reddish, green, or even bluish green in color, shows a distinct glassy luster, and if you see a very obvious conchoidal fracture, the rock is ....... OBSIDIAN

---

Granite, granite pegmatite, gabbro, diorite, basalt, scoria, felsite, pumice, and obsidian are IGNEOUS ROCKS.

Conglomerate, sandstone, shale, and limestone are SEDIMENTARY ROCKS.

Marble, schist, gneiss, slate, and quartzite are METAMORPHIC ROCKS.

**The Colorado Plateau** is one of the 14 physiographic provinces described in this chapter. It is a high region of mostly horizontal-lying sedimentary strata that have been sculptured by many rivers. The Grand Canyon, carved out by the Colorado River, and the Canyonlands section of central Utah, are good examples. Exposed rock of this province range in age from Precambrian to Recent. Intrusions of igneous rocks of Cenozoic age are widespread and their more resistant masses underlie such mountains as the Henry, La Sal, Abajo, and Navajo Mountains. About 15,000 square miles of the province are covered with volcanic rocks. The most well-known area is the San Francisco Mountains in north-central Arizona. Here, eruptions occurred from Middle Tertiary time to as recently as A.D. 1190 at Sunset Crater.

# 5  Rocks that Make Our Landscape

The landscape of the United States varies from low plains to high mountains and plateaus that have been cut by deep valleys and canyons. Each large region of land is a natural division of the continent, and, in general, it has the same kind of bedrock and surface shape. As such, each region is contrasted with other regions with different kinds of bedrock, surface shape, or history of development. Geologists call such regions of land **physiographic provinces.**

The physiographic provinces of the United States are shown on the map on pages 56 and 57. The various provinces are separated from each other on the map by color tints. Since these are *physiographic* provinces, they have nothing to do with state boundaries. As you read the map, you will see numbers ranging from 1 through 44 scattered over it. The numbers indicate only some of the more outstanding places where you can find the various kinds of rocks, minerals, and fossils listed in the "Guide to the Physiographic Provinces."

The colored line across the northern part of the physiographic province map marks the southern limit reached by advancing glaciers in the last Ice Age. In the area north of this line, you may find many examples of glacial

# GUIDE TO THE PHYSIOGRAPHIC PROVINCES AND

Numbers in the key below refer to the numbers on the Physiographic Map of the United States shown on this page. The numbers indicate some of the places to look for certain rocks, minerals, and fossils.

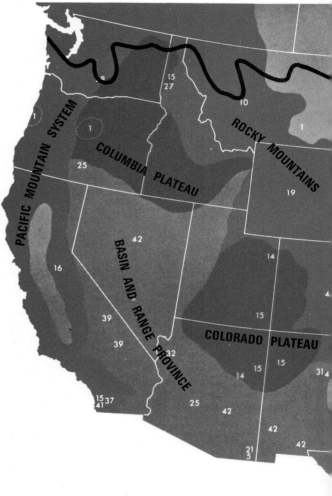

## 1 AGATE

MONTANA near Billings (along the Yellowstone River)

NORTH DAKOTA Williams County and McKenzie County (in gravels of the Yellowstone River and Missouri River)

OREGON coast and central area

SOUTH DAKOTA Custer County

TEXAS near Alpine, Brewster County; Mason County, Mason

## 2 AMAZONITE

COLORADO Teller County, Florissant

## 3 AMBER

MISSISSIPPI Tishomingo County and Tallahatchie County

## 4 AQUAMARINE (Beryl)

COLORADO Chaffee County, Mount Antero

## 5 AZURITE

ARIZONA Bisbee

## 6 BAUXITE

ARKANSAS Saline County, Bauxite

till. This consists of gravel and boulders of different kinds of rock carried from the north by glaciers.

As you read the brief text passages describing the topography, or shape, of the physical features of the land, and the types of rock found in each province, you will find frequent mention of igneous, sedimentary, and metamorphic rock. For a description of these rocks, see Chapter 3.

## TO SOME OUTSTANDING COLLECTING SITES

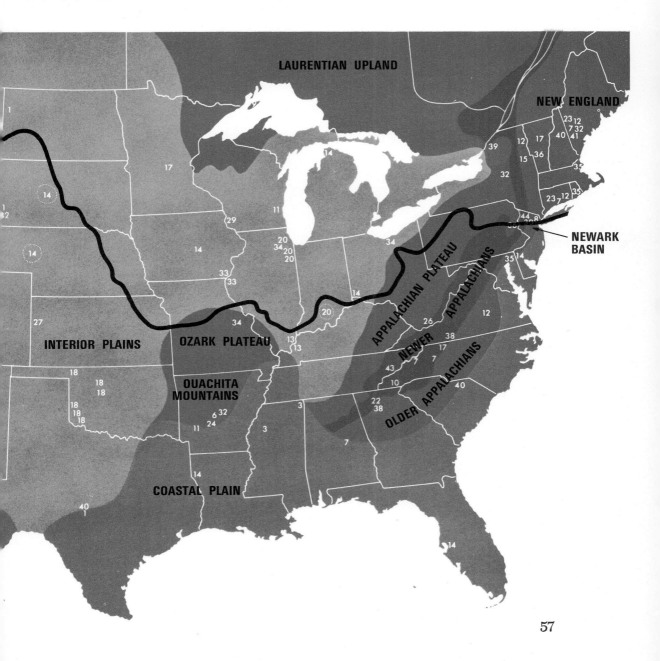

## 7 BERYL

ALABAMA Coosa County, near Hissop

CONNECTICUT Middletown

MAINE Oxford County, Paris

NORTH CAROLINA Alexander County, Shelby and Mitchell County, Spruce Pine

## 8 CALCITE (Fluorescent)

NEW JERSEY Passaic County, Paterson

## 9 CHLORASTROLITE (Greenstone)

MICHIGAN Isle Royal in Lake Superior

## 10 CORUNDUM

MONTANA near Helena

NORTH CAROLINA Macon County

## 11 DIAMOND

ARKANSAS Murfreesboro (Ouachita Mountains)

WISCONSIN Washington County, Kohlsville (in glacial till)

## 12 FELDSPAR

CONNECTICUT Middletown

MAINE Oxford County, Paris

NEW YORK Keesville

VIRGINIA Amelia

## 13 FLUORITE

ILLINOIS Rosiclare

KENTUCKY Crittenden County

## 14 FOSSILS

ARIZONA Holbrook (petrified wood)

COLORADO Teller County, Florissant (fossil insects)

DELAWARE New Castle County, along banks at canal (fossil invertebrates)

FLORIDA Hillsborough County, Tampa Bay (silicified coral)

IOWA Le Grand (fossil invertebrates)

LOUISIANA DeSoto Parish (petrified wood)

MICHIGAN Emmet County, Petoskey (coral)

NEBRASKA western (early mammals)

OHIO Cincinnati (fossil invertebrates)

SOUTH DAKOTA (early mammals)

UTAH Vernal (dinosaurs)

WYOMING fossil fish throughout state; Como Bluff (dinosaurs); southwestern part of state (petrified wood)

## 15 GARNET

ARIZONA Apache County

CALIFORNIA San Diego County, Pala

IDAHO Benawah County

NEW MEXICO McKinley County

NEW YORK North Creek (Gore Mountain)

UTAH San Juan County

## 16 GOLD

CALIFORNIA Calavaras County

## 17 GRANITE

MINNESOTA St. Cloud

NORTH CAROLINA Mount Airy

VERMONT Barre

## 18 GYPSUM

OKLAHOMA Beckham, Blaine, Greer, Harper, Jackson, and major counties

## 19 JADE

WYOMING Lander

## 20 LIMESTONE

ILLINOIS near Chicago, Joliet, and Kankakee

INDIANA south-central

## 21 MALACHITE

ARIZONA Bisbee

## 22 MARBLE

GEORGIA Pickens County

VERMONT Proctor

## 23 MICA

CONNECTICUT Middletown

MAINE Oxford County, Paris

**24 NOVACULITE (Whetstone)**

ARKANSAS Hot Springs County
(Ouachita Mountains)

**25 OBSIDIAN**

ARIZONA Maricopa County

OREGON Lake County

**26 ONYX, MEXICAN (variety of Calcite)**

WEST VIRGINIA Mercer County, near
Willowtown

**27 OPAL**

IDAHO Latah County, Whelan

KANSAS Wallace County, Wallace

**28 OPALIZED WOOD**

WASHINGTON Yakima County

**29 PEARL**

WISCONSIN Prairie du Chien
(Mississippi River)

**30 PREHNITE**

NEW JERSEY Passaic County, Paterson

**31 PUMICE**

NEW MEXICO north-central area, and
Valles Mountains west of Santa Fe

**32 QUARTZ**

ARIZONA near Kingman

ARKANSAS Little Rock (Ouachita
Mountains)

MAINE Oxford County

NEW YORK Herkimer County,
Middleville

SOUTH DAKOTA Custer

**33 QUARTZ GEODES (Quartz crystals inside a ball of chalcedony)**

ILLINOIS Warsaw

IOWA Keokuk

**34 SANDSTONE**

ILLINOIS southwest of Chicago

MISSOURI west of St. Louis

OHIO Lorain County

**35 SERPENTINE**

MARYLAND Cecil County, Rock Springs

MASSACHUSETTS Essex County,
Newburyport

RHODE ISLAND near Limerock north of
North Providence

**36 SLATE**

PENNSYLVANIA Bangor-Pen Argyl

VERMONT Poultney

**37 SPODUMENE**

CALIFORNIA San Diego County, Pala

**38 STAUROLITE**

GEORGIA Cherokee County, Ball Ground

VIRGINIA Stuart, Patrick County,
northwest Henry County, and Franklin
County

**39 TALC**

CALIFORNIA Inyo County, and Northern
San Bernardino County

NEW YORK Gouverneur and Talcville

**40 TOPAZ**

NEW HAMPSHIRE just south of boundary
between Carroll County and Coos
County, near North Chatham

SOUTH CAROLINA Chesterfield County,
Jefferson

TEXAS Mason County, Mason

**41 TOURMALINE**

CALIFORNIA San Diego County, Pala

MAINE Oxford County

**42 TURQUOISE**

ARIZONA Globe-Miami

NEVADA Lander County, Cortez

NEW MEXICO Santa Fe, Grant County
and Otero County

**43 UNAKITE**

TENNESSEE Cocke County and Sevier
County

**44 WILLEMITE (Fluorescent)**

NEW JERSEY Sussex County, Franklin

# PHYSIOGRAPHIC PROVINCES OF THE UNITED STATES

The photographs beginning on this page and continuing to page 69 show representative land features of the physiographic provinces keyed on the map on pages 56 and 57 and described in the captions here.

**Pacific Mountain System**   This province contains all three rock types. There are sedimentary and volcanic rocks of Tertiary age in the mountains of the Pacific Coast Ranges.

The Cascades are complex mountains with many high volcanic peaks also of Tertiary age. These include such famous mountains as Rainier and Shasta, which rise more than 14,000 feet above sea level. Lassen Peak, which became active in 1914 and continues to emit gases, is the only volcano in the continental United States which may be considered active. And within the large crater (technically called a **caldera**) of Mount Mazama in northern Oregon lies Crater Lake. This is one of the most beautiful lakes in the United States, having a depth of 2,000 feet. Wizard Island, a little volcano, rises above the lake's surface from the floor of the caldera.

The Sierra Nevada Mountains are composed mostly of intrusive igneous rock of granitic composition formed during late Mesozoic and early Cenozoic time. They have since been exposed to view by erosion.

**Columbia Plateau** Horizontal layers of basaltic lava flows, totaling more than 5000 feet in thickness and ranging in age from Early Tertiary to Pleistocene, form this province. The flows cover an area of about 200,000 square miles in Washington, Oregon, and Idaho and represent one of the great lava extrusions of geologic history. Beneath the flows are older, worn-down mountains. Spectacular canyons have been carved through this plateau by rivers such as the Snake and Columbia.

**Basin and Range Province**  The many isolated mountain ranges forming this province are separated from each other by inter-mountain basins. The ranges and basins were formed largely by vertical movements along **fault** zones—lines of weakness in the Earth's crust. Blocks that now are the mountain ranges rose, while the blocks now forming the basins sank. These major movements occurred near the end of the Tertiary Period—about 20 million years ago. The various ranges forming this province are often less than 100 miles long and are up to 15 miles wide. Although sediments washed down by rivers from the adjacent mountains fill the basins, the mountains contain mostly sedimentary and igneous rocks. The tops of the mountain ranges are often covered by hundreds of feet of lava flows, mostly of felsite. Igneous intrusions into the sedimentary rocks in many areas have formed valuable ore deposits of copper, zinc, lead, gold, and silver. Many ghost-towns in this province, such as Tombstone in southeastern Arizona, mark the sites of once prosperous mining towns.

**Rocky Mountains** Many complex mountain ranges and some inter-mountain basins (basins that lie between mountain ranges) make up this province. The ranges were formed by the folding and breaking of the Earth's crust in late Mesozoic and early Cenozoic time. Igneous, sedimentary, and metamorphic rocks are found throughout the Rocky Mountains province. Great thicknesses of volcanic rock occur in the Yellowstone Plateau and adjacent Absaroka Mountains. They range in age from Early Tertiary to Pleistocene.

**Interior Plains**   This sprawling province is a gently rolling region of horizontal layers of sedimentary rocks. Long cliffs are formed by the edges of layers that have resisted erosion. Erosion-resisting rocks form small, isolated highland areas, such as the Black Hills of South Dakota.

**Ozark Plateau and Ouachita Mountains**   The Ozark Plateau is like the Cumberland Plateau. Sedimentary rocks range in age from Cambrian to Pennsylvanian. The Ouachita Mountains contain folded sedimentary strata like those of the Newer Appalachians and range in age from Cambrian (most likely) to Pennsylvanian.

**Appalachian Plateau** This province was formed by the uplift of horizontal layers of sedimentary rocks like those of the Folded Appalachians. In places, the rocks have been so deeply carved by streams, that the topography is commonly termed mountainous. This province includes the Catskill, Pocono, Allegheny, and Cumberland Plateaus. The eastern margin of the Appalachian Plateau is indicated by a bold and rather sheer cliff. This **escarpment**, which forms the fronts of the Catskill, Pocono, Allegheny, and Cumberland Plateaus, is probably the longest and most nearly continuous land feature in the United States. The northern part was once covered by glaciers. Many fossils, from the Devonian to the early Permian Periods, can be found in this province. The oldest forest known to science existed here during the Devonian Period. Its fossil remains were discovered in the sedimentary strata of the Catskill Plateau near Gilboa, New York.

**Coastal Plain** This is a region of flat-lying layers of sedimentary strata that were once part of the ocean floor at the southwestern and eastern margin of the continent. It is now exposed above the present shoreline. Fossils, as old as early Cretaceous, can be found throughout the Coastal Plain. Capes Kennedy and Hatteras, Miami Beach, and Padre Island, among others, are examples of the many slender barrier beaches of recent sand deposits. The deposits were formed by wave action occurring a short distance offshore.

**Newer (Folded) Appalachians** The mountains comprising this province were formed by the bending and some breaking of layers of sedimentary rocks. There are long, slender ridges of harder rocks, such as sandstone and conglomerate, and parallel valleys of limestone and shale. Glacial till occurs only in the northern part of this province. Many fossils of invertebrate sea animals (sea animals without backbones) from the Cambrian to the Devonian Periods are found in these sedimentary rocks.

**Older Appalachians**   This province is similar to the New England Upland
Province, but there are no signs of glaciation. The Blue Ridge Mountains and a
lower, rolling area, called the Piedmont, are the two sections of this province.
The geologic age of this province is similar to that of the New England Upland
Province.

**Newark Basin** Lying between the two southward projections of the New England Upland Province and the two northward projections of the Older Appalachians is the Newark Basin. This province is composed almost entirely of a thick accumulation of sandstone and shale. Generally red in color because they contain quite a lot of red color-producing iron oxide, these sedimentary strata accumulated above sea level. Layered with these strata are basalt lava flows that form the Watchung Mountains, and an exposed igneous intrusion of diabase called the Palisades. Fossils of land-living animals (mostly reptiles) and fresh-water fish indicate that these rocks formed during the Triassic Period of the Earth's history, about 195 million years ago.

**Laurentian Upland** Many periods of mountain-building, followed by erosion, affected the rocks of these very old and complex mountains. The rocks are largely metamorphic, contain many igneous intrusions, and are Precambrian in age. (See geologic time chart, page 107.) The Adirondack Mountains in New York State are an extension of this province into the United States from Canada. The rather durable rock of that part of the Laurentians crossing into New York State form the famous Thousand Islands in the St. Lawrence Valley. Glacial till covers the region. The more than 2,000 lakes and ponds that occur in the Adirondacks were formed largely by glacial erosion or rock and soil debris carried by the glaciers which were left behind and dammed sections of the stream courses as the glaciers melted away.

**New England Upland Province** This is a region of metamorphic rock with many igneous intrusions. It also has gone through several stages of mountain-building and erosion. The rocks are not quite so old as those in the Laurentian Upland; they appear to be mostly of early Paleozoic age. Glaciers have also left their imprint on the lands of this province. Mt. Washington shown here.

Oil geologists survey part of their outdoor "laboratory," an area of Utah.

# 6 How to Read Topographic and Geologic Maps

Chances are that you do not live near one of the rich collecting areas shown on the Physiographic Map on page 56. Even so, there are ways that you can locate rock and mineral collecting areas near your home, or along the route to a place you are planning to visit. **Topographic** and **geologic** maps are two excellent guides to rock and mineral hunting grounds.

## TOPOGRAPHIC MAPS

By learning to read a topographic map, you will be able to tell a great deal about how an area looks without actually seeing it. Although a road map shows you certain things about an area, a topographic map shows many more details—such as the ups and downs of the land, the direction in which rivers and streams flow, valleys, mountains, and cliffs; also man-made things such as roads, towns, bridges, mines, and quarries.

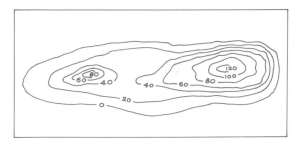 

Side view of an island (right), seen as a topographic map (at left).

The word topographic comes from two Greek words: *topos,* meaning "place," and *graphien,* meaning "to write." A topographic map shows the ups and downs of the land, or the topography, by **contour lines.** Each contour line of a topographic map marks a certain height, or elevation, above sea level. Every point on the same contour line is at the same elevation. To find out more about contour lines, let's examine the topographic map of an island with two hills.

The outside contour line is at sea level and outlines the coast line, so the elevation of this contour line is sea level, 0 feet. Each of the other contour lines is 20 feet higher above sea level than the one outside it. Since the highest point on the island is 132 feet above sea level, only seven contour lines need be drawn. By comparing the side view of the island with the topographic map, you can see how the map shows the shape *and* the elevation of the island.

## HOW TO MAKE CONTOUR LINES

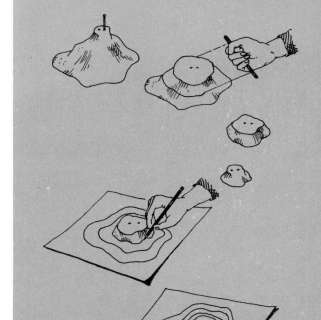

Make an island of modeling clay. Push a knitting needle or other small stick straight down through the clay at two high points of the island, leaving two holes. Next, slice horizontal layers of equal thickness by pushing a wire cheese-cutter, or a piece of thin wire, through the clay. Now lay the bottom slice on a sheet of paper and trace its outline on the paper. Make pencil dots through each of the two holes. Remove the bottom layer of clay and place the second layer on the paper, lining up the holes in the layer with the dots on the paper. Trace the outline of this layer, then the outlines of each smaller layer, in the same way. Your tracings are a contour map of the island.

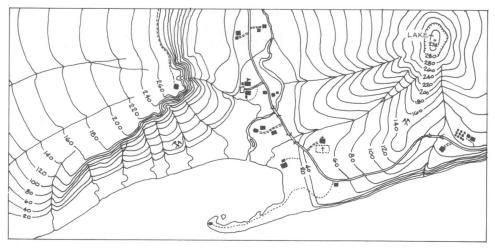

This topographic map shows, in addition to the natural ups and downs of the land, such man-made features as buildings, churches, and roads.

Let us now turn to another topographic map, one that shows many other features. Look at the map above. It shows an area that has mountains, a volcano with a lake in its crater at the summit, rivers, cliffs, and other natural features. This topographic map also shows some man-made features. Here are some important things to learn about reading a topographic map:

Shore lines of oceans and lakes are *natural* contour lines, rarely falling exactly on a given contour line. For example, because the lake shore inside the crater of the volcano is 274 feet above sea level, its natural contour line falls between the contour lines for 260 and 280 feet.

T  All points on a given contour line *always* have the same height above sea level.

T  Contour lines never cross each other. This is because a point on the map cannot, for example, be both 200 and 220 feet above sea level.

T  Where contour lines are close together, the slope of the hill is steep.

T  Where contour lines are far apart, the slope is gentle.

T  Contour lines always curve upstream in river valleys, forming a clear V-shaped pattern. By looking carefully at the volcano topographic map, can you tell the directions of flow for any of the streams? A stream flows opposite to the direction in which the V-shaped pattern of the contour lines points in the valley.

T  Contour lines that are closed within the map area represent hills.

T  Contour lines that are shown with **hachure** marks, like this ⌦⎯⎯⎯⎯⊃ , mean that there is a basin-shaped depression in the landscape. Can you find such depression contour lines? Notice that the elevations *inside* the crater of the volcano are *lower* than the elevations near the rim of the crater.

If you write away for a topographic map, first ask for the free *Index Circular* of the topographic maps available for the state you are interested in. To do this, see page 116 for further information about whom to write. The *Index*

72

*Circular* is a map of the entire state with rectangles printed on it. The rectangles correspond to the published topographic maps (also called **quadrangles**). The *Index Circular* also tells you when the topographic map was made, its scale, whether the map is still in print, how to order it, and other information. You will find that almost the entire state you are interested in has been topographically mapped. But some of the maps may have been prepared fifty or more years ago and are probably out-of-date. However, even such old maps are often very useful. After you have ordered the map or maps you want, you will receive one that looks very much like the topographic map reproduced on the front endpapers (in color).

Study this map carefully. Are you able to tell the steep hills from the gentle slopes? Can you find a depression, a valley, a lake? Can you tell which way the streams are flowing? Here is some other information printed on topographic maps:

T The **scale**, or map-to-ground distance, is printed at the bottom of every map. Usually the scale is 1:62,500—meaning that one inch on the map equals 62,500 inches (or about one mile) on the ground. A scale of 1:31,000 would mean that one inch on the map equals 31,000 inches (or about ½ mile) on the ground. What is the scale of the topographic map reproduced in this book? Maps with large scales cover *less* ground than smaller scaled maps. A topographic map with a scale of 1:31,000 covers less ground than a map with a scale of 1:62,500. But a topographic map with a large scale of 1:31,000 shows much greater detail than a map having a smaller scale of 1:62,500.

T Any location on the map can be read in degrees of latitude and longitude, which are printed along the edges of the map.

T Contour lines are printed in brown. Every fifth line, called an **index contour**, is printed in dark brown. The elevation in feet is printed somewhere along these index contours. The vertical distance between contour lines, called the **contour interval**, is always printed at the bottom of the map. The lower the value of the contour interval, the greater will be the topographic detail visible to you.

T Man-made features such as buildings, boundary lines, mines, quarries, and so on are printed in black (see following page). Although most roads are also in black, the more modern four- to six-lane highways are usually shown in red.

T Water areas are shown in blue.

T Areas of natural forests are frequently shown in solid green.

T The top of the map is always north. East is to the right, west to the left, and south to the bottom. If you are facing south, hold the map so that the bottom (south) end is away from you, or pointing south. In other words, you should hold and read the map upside down. If you face west, make sure that you hold the map so that west on the map faces west, and so on. This is called **orienting** a map. Any map should always be properly oriented so that you can easily compare shapes and direction on the map with the shapes and directions of the real features you are trying to identify.

# TOPOGRAPHIC MAP SYMBOLS

## VARIATIONS WILL BE FOUND ON OLDER MAPS

Hard surface, heavy duty road, four or more lanes

Hard surface, heavy duty road, two or three lanes

Hard surface, medium duty road, four or more lanes

Hard surface, medium duty road, two or three lanes

Improved light duty road

Unimproved dirt road—Trail

Dual highway, dividing strip 25 feet or less

Dual highway, dividing strip exceeding 25 feet

Road under construction

Railroad: single track—multiple track

Railroads in juxtaposition

Narrow gage: single track—multiple track

Railroad in street—Carline

Bridge: road—railroad

Drawbridge: road—railroad

Footbridge

Tunnel: road—railroad

Overpass—Underpass

Important small masonry or earth dam

Dam with lock

Dam with road

Canal with lock

Buildings (dwelling, place of employment, etc.)

School—Church—Cemeteries

Buildings (barn, warehouse, etc.)

Power transmission line

Telephone line, pipeline, etc. (labeled as to type)

Wells other than water (labeled as to type)                 o Oil          o Gas

Tanks; oil, water, etc. (labeled as to type)                 ● ● ●    ⊘ Water

Located or landmark object—Windmill                            o            ⸸

Open pit, mine, or quarry—Prospect                             ⚒            x

Shaft—Tunnel entrance                                          ◪            Y

Horizontal and vertical control station:

    tablet, spirit level elevation                              BM △ 3899

    other recoverable mark, spirit level elevation                △ 3938

Horizontal control station: tablet, vertical angle elevation          VABM △ 2914

    any recoverable mark, vertical angle or checked elevation          △ 5675

Vertical control station: tablet, spirit level elevation              BM × 945

    other recoverable mark, spirit level elevation                × 890

Checked spot elevation                                        × 5923

Unchecked spot elevation—Water elevation                      × 5657        870

Boundary: national

    state

    county, parish, municipio

    civil township, precinct, town, barrio

    incorporated city, village, town, hamlet

    reservation, national or state

    small park, cemetery, airport, etc.

    land grant

Township or range line, U.S. land survey

Township or range line, approximate location

Section line, U.S. land survey

Section line, approximate location

Township line, not U.S. land survey

Section line, not U.S. land survey

Section corner: found—indicated                              +

Boundary monument: land grant—other                          □         o

U.S. mineral or location monument                            ▲

| Index contour | | Intermediate contour |
|---|---|---|
| Supplementary contour | | Depression contours |
| Fill | | Cut |
| Levee | | Levee with road |
| Mine dump | | Wash |
| Tailings | | Tailings pond |
| Strip mine | | Distorted surface |
| Sand area | | Gravel beach |

| Perennial streams | | Intermittent streams |
|---|---|---|
| Elevated aqueduct | → ← | Aqueduct tunnel |
| Water well—Spring | o          o~ | Disappearing stream |
| Small rapids | | Small falls |
| Large rapids | | Large falls |
| Intermittent lake | | Dry lake |
| Foreshore flat | | Rock or coral reef |
| Sounding—Depth curve | 10 | Piling or dolphin |
| Exposed wreck | | Sunken wreck |
| Rock, bare or awash—dangerous to navigation | | |

| Marsh (swamp) | | Submerged marsh |
|---|---|---|
| Wooded marsh | | Mangrove |
| Woods or brushwood | | Orchard |
| Vineyard | | Scrub |

Once you have learned to read a topographic map, you can use it to locate promising spots to collect rocks and minerals. For example, investigate areas where close-spaced contour lines are shown on your map. There will probably be exposed rock on those steep slopes. Rivers often expose rock in the walls of their valleys. You may find the symbol for a mine or quarry on your map. Mine dumps are heaps of broken waste rock removed from a mine. They are good places to collect specimens. Always mark your collecting sites on your map. The value of a specimen is almost entirely lost if you do not know where it came from. Let us now turn to another kind of map that will help you in your collecting.

## GEOLOGIC MAPS

Another kind of map that you will find very useful is the geologic map (see back endpapers). A geologic map is one that shows the location of different kinds of bedrock of the Earth's crust. **Bedrock** is the continuously solid rock beneath the cover of vegetation, soil, or broken rock. The places where bedrock happens to be exposed to view are called **outcrops**. Studying the outcrops of the bedrock and making geologic maps of an area is the main job of the field geologist.

A geologic map is made by drawing on a topographic map the outlines of

Outcrop of the bedrock underlying the soil in Central Park, New York City.

the different rock units that occur in a given area. **A rock unit** is a single mass of rock that is different from neighboring masses of rock. For example, an outcrop of sandstone is a unit quite different from an outcrop of granite. The many different rock units, which you will soon come to recognize as units, were formed during various times in the Earth's very long history.

In doing his surveying, the field geologist first makes a record of exactly where various rock units are, and how far and in what directions they extend. This information is then entered on his topographic map so that he can relate it to such landscape features as hills and valleys. The positions of rock units are also shown in relation to other map features, such as buildings and roads. To make these different rock units very noticeable on a geologic map, a coded symbol and different color is used for each different rock unit.

The basic rock unit on a geologic map is called a **formation.** A formation is a unit of rock that is usually easily recognizable because it shows a set of distinctive features; for example, color, its mineral content, the kind of rock (such as shale, granite, gneiss, and so on), and the particular kinds of fossils it may contain. In other words, any "formation" has a general physical appearance that is different from the physical appearance of neighboring formations. A formation is usually named after the geographic locality near which it was first identified—*Potsdam* sandstone, or *Chattanooga* shale.

The term formation is applied to igneous and metamorphic rock units, as well as to sedimentary rock units. The Storm King granite or the Cave Creek Canyon formation are formations of igneous rock; the Pinal schist and the Manhattan formation are formations of metamorphic rock.

Now let us turn to the geologic map reproduced on the back endpapers. Notice that the topographic map appearing on the front endpapers was used as the base map. The positions of the different rock formations are always shown in relation to the features of the landscape. Notice also the *Explanation* on the right side of the map. In the *Explanation* on the geologic map, the rock formations are very briefly described, and they are always arranged according to their relative age. The oldest ones are at the bottom of the list; the younger formations are near the top. The times when these rock formations originated—during the Paleozoic Era, the Triassic Period, and so on— is always shown. (In a later chapter, we will have much more to say about geologic time and what these names mean.)

How can a geologic map help you in your collecting? Imagine that you are traveling along a highway with your family, or with friends from a local collecting club. You know exactly where you are on this road because you are following your trip route very carefully on a geologic map. Suddenly someone spots an outcrop of a rock formation. Should you stop to investigate or just keep on going? From the color code and coded symbol on the geologic map, and from the information in the *Explanation* opposite that color code, you learn that the rock exposed on the side of the road is an outcrop of, let us say, the Denver formation. The brief description in the *Explanation* on the geologic map tells you that this formation is quite rich in fossils. So you will probably want to stop to collect fossils. By being able to read a geologic map, you will be able to obtain valuable information quickly.

## SOME STANDARD GEOLOGIC CROSS-SECTION SYMBOLS

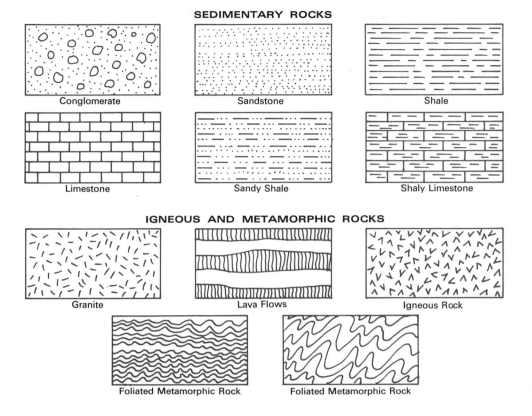

### SEDIMENTARY ROCKS

Conglomerate  Sandstone  Shale

Limestone  Sandy Shale  Shaly Limestone

### IGNEOUS AND METAMORPHIC ROCKS

Granite  Lava Flows  Igneous Rock

Foliated Metamorphic Rock  Foliated Metamorphic Rock

A geologic map shows one other thing that is important to you—a **geologic cross-section** (also shown on the back endpapers). You can imagine a geologic cross-section as one wall of a very deep trench—maybe 1000 or 2000 feet deep —cut straight down into the Earth's crust. It is not unlike cutting a slice out of a thick layer cake. When you remove the piece, each layer is clearly visible. A geologic cross-section shows how the rocks would appear below the Earth's surface if you could see them.

On our geologic map in this book, the cross-section shows the rock formations as they would appear along a certain line. Standard symbols are used on all geologic cross-sections for different kinds of rock types.

The variety of coded information on a geologic map clearly shows the distinctive rock formations in a given region. You can see where any rock formation occurs on the earth's surface, its length and width, and its relationship to adjacent rock formations. By studying a geologic cross-section, you can see how the rocks are arranged and how their formations appear at various depths. Unfortunately, geologic maps are not available for many regions in the United States. It takes many years to study a region carefully and then prepare a map of its geology. When geologic maps are available, they usually accompany a survey report made by the geologist. A survey report describes in great detail all that has been learned about the geology of a region.

In addition to the federal government, each state government prepares geologic survey reports and geologic maps of its own state. To order a geologic map and survey report, you must first know the name of the topographic base map. Then write to the appropriate state geological survey to find out if a geologic map for that *quadrangle* is available. (The addresses of all the state geological surveys are listed under Group A of the "Where-To-Find-It-Guide" beginning on page 116.)

When you go out to collect rocks, minerals, or fossils, first try to study a topographic or geologic map. By doing so, you will know exactly where to go in order to find certain types of rocks. Also, try to take at least a topographic map with you whenever you go on a collecting trip. The map will serve as a record of the areas where you collect. And don't forget, a map may help prevent you from getting lost if you are collecting in a strange area.

# 7 How to Collect Rocks and Minerals

It is now time to don gloves, goggles, and hammer and go out of doors to experience the thrill of discovering your own rock and mineral specimens. What is there about rocks and minerals that makes so many people enthusiastic collectors?

For the first time you are able to find out for yourself *why* so many things look the way they do in a landscape. The brilliant colors of the Yellowstone or Colorado Plateaus are caused by the minerals that make up the rocks. An interest in rocks and minerals will lead you to discover that the grains of sand on a beach or in a stream are not all white, or colorless. Some are black, others red, green, yellow. Where did they come from? If you try to find out, your search may lead you to the cliffs bordering the sea. Here you might find the source for only *some* of the sand grains. You might have to continue your search and explore the hills and mountains farther inland to discover

79

where some of the other sand grains came from. In the mountains you would find the rocks that are constantly being broken down by the forces of erosion, and the streams that carry their fragments to the edge of the sea. Continuing your search in the mountains, you might find an abandoned quarry which, until now, you thought of as nothing but a large hole in the ground. You could find yourself spending many pleasant hours examining the quarry's walls, or poking around in a nearby mine dump. With each expedition you will learn something new about the Earth and the forces that shape and reshape its surface.

## Where to look

Where can you find interesting rocks and minerals? The answer is anywhere you find outcrops—where the bedrock is exposed. You can find outcrops of the bedrock in many road and railroad cuts, where there are cliffs, quarry excavations, or in valleys where streams or glaciers have eroded courses through the bedrock.

If you live in a large city, you may find exposures of the bedrock where new buildings or bridges are being constructed, or where a tunnel is being cut through a solid rock formation. Always be on the lookout for such construction sites.

Outcrops may not be available where you live, but you can find rocks in other places. One of the best places to visit is a stone cutting factory. Here you will find fragments of granite or marble used in making monuments; or marble, limestone, serpentine, or a great variety of other rock used for table-tops or for decoration. You can also find many scattered rocks along the road-side, in the beds or along the banks of streams and rivers. And don't overlook beaches, where you may find beautiful water-tumbled rocks and pebbles.

Geologists frequently use the term **float** to describe rocks lying about, such as those shown in the photograph. But rocks comprising float are not necessarily part of the bedrock of the area where the float is found. For this reason

The rocks (lower right) in this photograph are not part of the local bedrock. They were carried from many miles away by glacial ice, and are called *float*.

80

the geologic story of the bedrock of a region cannot always be revealed by float. The float could have come from hundreds of miles away, and it may be completely different from the bedrock in the area you are studying. Many of the boulders found in New England and in the northern part of the United States were carried hundreds of miles southward by glaciers, then deposited where they now lie. However, these scattered New England rocks do tell a story. They show us the kind of bedrock the glaciers passed over during their long journey.

### Collecting rock samples

If you intend to become a serious collector, you must adopt a system of collecting, use the proper equipment, and keep records of your collecting trips.

Get a small notebook and keep a written record of where your specimens come from. Were they taken directly from the bedrock? Or were they part of the float? To know the locality of your specimens, you should have a topographic map. Even a common road map would be of some help. On the map carefully keep track of where you are along the road so that you know at all times exactly where you are collecting your specimens. You also will need a hammer to break off rock samples. A geologist's hammer will do the job best. You will also need a good steel chisel (one for chiseling metal) to split rocks apart, particularly if you are looking for fossils. A hand sledgehammer can be used to break off a small section of a large rock mass, which can then be trimmed with your regular hammer and chisel. A 10-power magnifying

June 10, 1964

WEATHER: Clear skies, afternoon convectional thunderstorms.

LOCATION: Dumppiles of the "Lucky Cuss" mine about 8 miles north of Bisbee Ariz. located at the Superstition mountains.

GENERAL GEOLOGY: Mine located in sedimentary rock that has been folded and faulted by past crustal upheavals. Granite intrusions into limestone have resulted in the formation of many interesting minerals - collected 35 specimens. These include granite (1-4) limestone (14-17) chalcopyrite (21-26) and sphalerite (33-35). No specimens were obtained from outcrops.

Went with the Tombstone Pebble-Pup Club

This is a sample notebook page showing the kinds of notes a good collector makes. Notice how to record the weather, date, what you collected, how the specimens are numbered, and who else was along on the trip.

OLD NEWSPAPERS
FIELD GUIDEBOOK
STEEL CHISELS
ADHESIVE TAPE
NONBREAKABLE GOGGLES
10-POWER MAGNIFYING LENS
BAND-AIDS
SPECIMEN BAG

CANTEEN WITH WATER
FIELD NOTEBOOK
PLASTIC CONTAINER
BALL-POINT PEN
PENCIL
TOPOGRAPHIC MAP
JACKKNIFE
COMPASS
GEOLOGIST'S HAMMER
HAND SLEDGEHAMMER

A well-equipped collector takes these items along on a field trip.

lens will give you a closer look at the details of your specimen. A good book describing rocks and minerals is also handy to have along.

If the outcrops you are breaking are particularly hard, wear gloves and non-breakable goggles. And make sure that you carefully wrap your specimens in newspaper before you pack them away in your knapsack or collecting bag. Delicate specimens can be put in well-padded plastic containers. Tape the loose ends of the paper with adhesive tape, number each specimen on the tape, then enter the number, date, and source of each specimen in your notebook. A rock sample should be no smaller than your hand. Take two or three samples of the same kind of rock. Taking more than one sample will give you a bigger collection, and you can find out more about rocks, minerals, and fossils by looking for individual differences in several samples of the same kind. Also, you can trade extra samples with other collectors.

Before making a collecting trip, plan it well. This is very important, for you must always know exactly where you are collecting. The value of a mineral or fossil is much less if you do not know where it came from.

If you take a long trip, stop and visit rock and mineral dealers along the way. They can tell you what kinds of rocks and minerals are found locally, and will often suggest good collecting sites. The names and addresses of rock and mineral dealers (as well as a number of good collecting areas) are given in the *Rockhound Buyer's Guide*. That and other books listing famous collecting sites in the United States are found on pages 119 and 120.

To protect the rock and mineral specimens you collect, wrap each one in a newspaper, as shown in this sequence of photographs.

Label each rock or mineral specimen with a letter symbol and number.

## Arranging your collection

After you have collected your specimens, try to arrange and study them right away. First, carefully brush away any soil, then wash each specimen in soapy, warm water. If the specimens are not too delicate, give them a good rubbing with a stiff brush. Next, identify your specimens by using the identification keys on pages 50 to 53. If you have an uncommon rock or mineral, you can check it in one of the rock and mineral guidebooks listed on page 121. Make sure you learn all you can about each rock, mineral, or fossil so that you will recognize each one the next time you see it, even though it may seem to have a slightly different appearance.

After you have identified a specimen, label it. To do this, put a spot of white

| | | |
|---|---|---|
| Collection of Tom Jones | | |
| SPECIMEN: Gneiss | CATALOG NO. Me-22 | |
| ANY ADDITIONAL MINERALS: | | |
| LOCALITY: Roadcut, Northside of Cross-Bronx Expressway, 500 feet west of Jerome Ave. Exit | | |
| REMARKS: Excellent garnet crystals embedded in biotite mica | | |
| ACQUIRED: In exchange for D-96 with Mary Smith, New York City | DATE: 7/14/66 | |

Gneiss                                             Me-22

   Sample of the Fordam formation contains quartz, feldspar, biotite mica and garnet

   Received in exchange for D-96 galena from the dump of the "Lucky Cuss" mine near Bisbee and collected June 10, 1966

Use file cards to record information about the specimens you collect.

enamel paint in a corner of the specimen. After the paint has dried, write a number on it with a fine-pointed pen. Cover the number with clear nail polish to keep it from flaking off.

There are many ways to arrange a rock and mineral collection. One way is to put the specimens in their alphabetical order. But this method has little scientific value. The specimens cannot be related to each other.

A better way is to arrange them according to basic types. For example, the letter **I** could stand for *igneous,* **S** for *sedimentary,* and **Me** for *metamorphic* rocks; **Mi** for *minerals*; and **F** for *fossils.* Number the specimens of the same type, 1, 2, 3, 4, and so on, and add your initials. Next get 3-by-5-inch file cards and write on each card all the information you have in your field notebook about a single specimen. This will be your catalog card. File it in numbered order with cards for other specimens of the same type.

Make another file card for each specimen, putting the name of the specimen in the upper left-hand corner of the card, and the catalog number of that specimen in the upper right-hand corner. Do this with each specimen and file the cards with the *names of the specimens* in alphabetical order.

Now, if anyone wants to see all of your quartz specimens, all you have to do is look up "quartz" in your alphabetical file. The cards under that subject will guide you to the quartz specimens in your collection. If someone wants additional information about any specimen—where you found it, say—your catalog file card has the information. As you collect more and more specimens, give away your poorer specimens to make room for better ones collected from similar sites, and trade your extras for new specimens. You may have to change this recording plan a little as more specimens are added to your collection. But as a beginning, this method should serve you well.

### Storing your collection

After you catalog your specimens, you will need a place to keep them. Cigar boxes make a good temporary storage place. Ask your local drugstore, candy store, or shopping center for some of their empty boxes. Use a strip of heavy cardboard to separate the two specimens you can store in each box. Old bookcases, chests of drawers, or china closets also are good places to store specimens. To keep your specimens from sliding around in a drawer, put each one in a shallow cardboard tray, which you can make or buy from a mineral dealer. Or, you can cut up an egg carton and use it to meet your storage needs.

As your interest in rocks, minerals, and fossils increases, you will be reading many books and magazines dealing with the subject. Perhaps you might subscribe to one or two of the earth science magazines listed on page 121. More important, get out into the outdoors yourself and see things for yourself rather than through the eyes of a teacher or author of a book. If you join a local mineral and rock club, you'll have many chances to take field and collecting trips with them.

Make note-taking a *habit*. Write down what you see, not what a book may tell you that you should be seeing. Don't be satisfied with just knowing the name of a mineral, rock, or fossil. Visit a museum of natural history, write to one of the universities in your state, or to your state geological survey for as much information as you can obtain. Most state geological surveys have free pamphlets on the rocks, minerals, and fossils of their own states, together with descriptions of outstanding collecting areas. Write for these publications. Find out all you can about any specimen. Soon you may become a local authority—not only of the rocks, minerals, or fossils of your area, but also of its general geology.

Mica schist, from New York City, with garnet crystals.

The fossils on this shale are all imprints of brachiopods, a shelled marine invertebrate that lived about 370 million years ago in what is now New York State.

# 8   Collecting Fossils—Links with the Past

Long before you were born, many thousands of different kinds of plants and animals had been living on our planet for millions and hundreds of millions of years. They appeared on the Earth long before the time of the rivers, lakes, mountains, and valleys familiar to us all today. We know that such plants and animals lived at various times during the Earth's primeval past because they left tell-tale marks. Today we call these records **fossils**. Some are only impressions left in sections of soft sediment that later became rock. Others are actual remains—of a tree trunk, or the bone of an animal—that have "turned into stone." Still other fossils are simply footprints or worm borings. Scientists who study fossils are called **paleontologists** (from the Greek word *palaios*, meaning "ancient," and *onta*, meaning "existing things," and *logos*, meaning "the study of").

The word fossil comes from the Latin word *fossilis*, meaning "dug up." For

Remains of trees that lived 190 million years ago. The wood has been replaced by colorful minerals such as red jasper and other quartz minerals.

many years any object dug up from the ground was called a "fossil," even such things as minerals. But today we think of fossils as the direct evidence of animals and plants buried naturally in the earth. To qualify as fossils, they must also be quite old—more than 10,000 years. At that time a huge glacier covering much of North America (see map on page 56), Europe, and Asia began to melt away. Because the time of glacial activity of the last Ice Age is known rather accurately, it provides the paleontologist with a convenient time peg. To qualify as a fossil, the plant or animal remains must pre-date the withdrawal of this extensive glacier, which occurred about 10,000 years ago.

### Where to look for fossils

How often have you passed an old quarry, or rock outcrops that highway engineers had to blast through? Or how many times have you seen rock exposed at the bottom of a creek bed? It is in such places, where rock of the

Earth's crust is exposed, that you should explore for fossils. But unfortunately, *all* exposed rocks do not contain fossils. Only those that were once sediments—mud, lime, or sand deposits on the floor of an ancient, shallow sea; or sand and mud left behind by long-vanished rivers, lakes, or swamps. Many different animals and plants lived, died, and were buried in such sediments. As time passed, more and more sediments formed over the older ones containing the dead plant or animal. After many years the sediment layers were squeezed together and cemented into hard rock. We find fossils, then, chiefly in sedimentary rock.

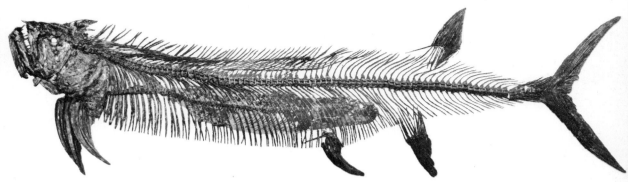

This fossil skeleton of a fourteen-foot, Late Cretaceous fish *(Portheus)* with a six-foot undigested fish inside *(Gillicus)* was unearthed in Kansas.

1

2

After swallowing *Gillicus, Portheus* died, sank to the bottom...

3

4

its skeleton was buried. Later, the sea withdrew and erosion exposed *Portheus.*

On very rare occasions, fossils have been found in igneous and metamorphic rocks. For example, the casts of trees have been found in lava flows, but such flows were quite cool at the time the tree was caught up in the lava, otherwise the tree would have been burned to ash. Also, if metamorphic rocks containing fossils have not been changed too much by heat and pressure, some of their fossils may be in reasonably good condition—such as those sometimes found in slate.

So, before setting out on a fossil hunt, you should first locate areas where sedimentary rocks are exposed. You can do this by checking a geologic map of the area you are planning to search. When you discover an area of sedimentary rock, don't be too disappointed if you don't find any fossils. Not all sedimentary rocks contain fossils. One reason is that few or no plants or animals might have been living at the time or place when those particular sediments were forming. Another reason is that fossil forming is a very complicated process. Perhaps only one out of every thousand or ten thousand plants or animals left a record of itself. The others decayed away completely without a trace.

### How to collect fossils

After you discover a likely fossil-collecting spot, make sure that you have a hammer with you. A bricklayer's hammer works very well. Also have one or two medium-sized tempered cold steel chisels, a knapsack, some old newspapers, adhesive tape, ball-point pen, a good map, a few plastic pill bottles with cotton to hold small or delicate specimens, and a small magnifying glass.

Wrap each specimen you collect in newspaper and tape the ends together (see page 83). On the adhesive tape write down a number and the date you found each fossil. In your notebook write down the number and the date for each fossil, a short description of the fossil (or its name if you know it), the kind of rock you found it in, and where you found it. Much of the value of a fossil is lost if you do not have this information.

When you are searching and collecting, try not to run quickly from one spot to another at the rock outcrop. Instead, spend some time looking carefully on your hands and knees or just sitting in one place. Turn over loose pieces of rock and carefully examine all sides of them. You will be surprised what you may find. Many excellent fossils have been found in places passed over many times by other fossil-hunters.

With your hammer and chisel, split the sedimentary rocks parallel to the layers, not across them. It is on the broad, flat surfaces between layers that the fossils will be found. Many fossils cannot be removed from the rock without being destroyed. So you may have to trim the rock down to a small size, keeping the fossil intact. Wrap the trimmed specimen in newspaper, then number and date it. Later, at home, you may possibly be able to free the fossil without destroying it. Should you find bones of vertebrate animals or any other fossils you think are rare, leave them intact and call for professional help. Many valuable fossils have been ruined by people not experienced in removing them.

Label each fossil for your collection with a letter symbol and number.

## Preparing your fossils

After you have brought your specimens home and have unwrapped them, make sure that you don't misplace the adhesive tape and its number. Place the specimens in water and let them soak overnight. Excess rock and soil can then be removed with a stiff toothbrush. You can then use long needles, tweezers, or old dental picks from your dentist to clean around the smaller structures of your fossil. With the dental pick you may even remove much of the rock around the fossil, but work very carefully whenever you pick away at the rock next to the fossil.

After cleaning a fossil, you should then label and catalog it. One way of arranging your collection is to group all the fossils from one collecting area, then give each fossil a number. You could designate each collecting area by a different letter. The letter and specimen number are then painted on the fossil. In numbering your specimen, follow the instructions on page 84. Much of the information you find out about the fossil should go on a special label, together with the catalog number, and be placed beneath the fossil in its storage tray. This information, plus all the additional data you have in your field notes, and information you get from other sources, should all be transcribed on a 3-by-5-inch file card. These catalog cards, one for each fossil, can then be arranged in numerical order within each group and kept in your files. A fossil without such information is little more than a curio and is of no scientific value.

Specimen No. _D-27_

Name _Neospirifer cameratus_

Rock Formation _Columbia limestone_

Age _Middle Pennsylvanian_

Locality _Apple Orchard Creek_
_Athens County, Ohio_
_(800 feet northwest of John Doe's farm house)_

Collector _Samuel B. Smith_

Date _July 5, 1966_

Use file cards to record information about the specimens you collect.

91

Several complete skeletons of a small, primitive dinosaur, *Coelophysis,* discovered at Ghost Ranch, near Abiquiu, New Mexico.

### How fossils are formed

Let us turn now to the question of how a fossil is formed. The sedimentary layers of the Earth's crust are a vast graveyard. In them lie the scattered remains of the living creatures that once wandered over the Earth's surface, or grew in its primeval soil. Did you ever wonder how fossils are formed? Why didn't the animal or plant simply decay away entirely without leaving a record of itself?

An animal or plant may become a fossil if some part of it is tough enough to be preserved, some part that does not decay away very quickly, such as bone, shell, or hard wood. But hardness alone is not enough. The hard part must be buried quite quickly, or else it, too, will decay. Also, the plant or animal must remain rather undisturbed during the time it is being fossilized.

In a few unusual and rare cases, some very special condition has helped preserve almost the entire animal. Extreme cold or extreme dryness are such special conditions. Almost entire fossil mammoths have been found preserved in frozen ground, completely refrigerated for more than 25,000 years in Siberia and Alaska. And in dry regions of South America, parts of mummified ground sloths have been found preserved in dry and protected caves. But these are rare cases.

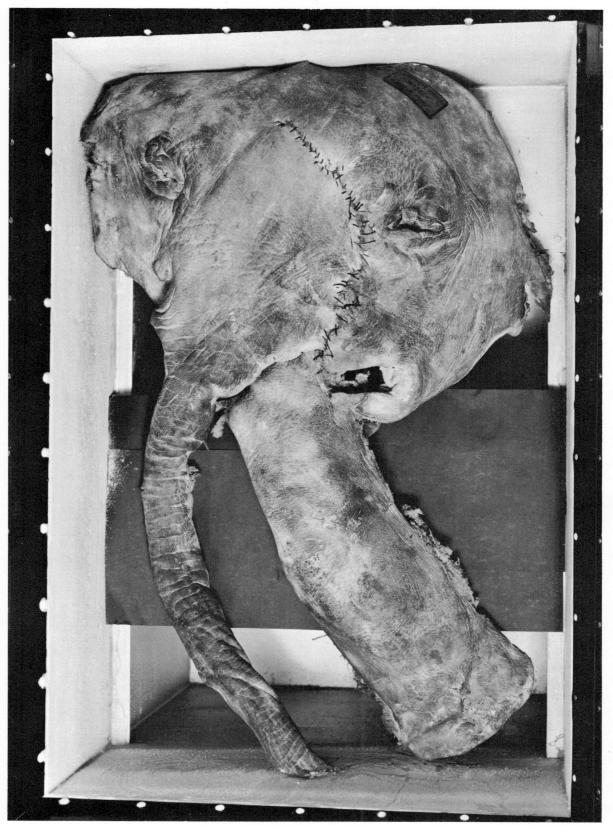

The trunk, head, and forelimb of a remarkably well-preserved baby woolly mammoth, which was dug out of frozen ground in Alaska.

Many of the plants and animals that are now part of our fossil record were preserved as their bone, shell, or other hard parts were changed into a different substance. Mineral-bearing water slowly seeping downward through the sediments was soaked up by the porous bones, shells, or wood. Gradually the minerals left behind (after the water evaporated) filled the small open spaces within the bone or shell. The addition of minerals tends to make the bone, shell, or wood even harder. Very often the actual bone or shell is dissolved by the ground water. When this happens, the minerals in the water slowly replace the bones, shells, or wood as they are being dissolved. Brightly colored silica, calcite, or orange and red iron compounds often become part of fossil bone or shell. In some petrified wood, silica has not only filled in small hollow spaces, but has replaced the once-living woody tissue. This has happened so perfectly that the individual cells and annual rings show up very exactly and clearly many, many millions of years later.

The petrified log on the facing page was formed millions of years ago by a process of mineral replacement. As the top diagram shows, the log was buried by sediments. Over the centuries, mineral-bearing water (shown in color) seeping down through the sediments was soaked up by the wood. Gradually the wood was dissolved away and only the hardened minerals were left (bottom diagram).

94

A fossil *mold*, or hollow impression (top), of a marine shell is left in rock.

A *cast* of the fossil is made when minerals fill the mold and solidify.

Many fossils are merely traces—impressions in stone—of past life. After the plant or animal died it was quickly buried in the sediment. Gradually, the hard parts as well as the soft parts dissolved or decayed. Only a cavity or hollow space was left in the sedimentary rock where the shell or other hard part once lay. The walls of such cavities become a natural copy, or **mold**, of the shell or other skeletal part. Millions of years after the cavity is formed, minerals seep into and refill the cavity. In this way, a natural **cast** of the original mold is formed, and centuries later may be dug up by a lucky fossil hunter. Molds and casts are very common fossil forms—particularly for the invertebrates.

Occasionally the hard outside skeleton and tiny appendages of insects have been discovered in **amber**, the hardened and fossilized resin of ancient trees. Sometimes plants and small, soft-bodied organisms living in the seas have been buried in mud which hardened into shale. But in these cases, the only remains are a thin film of carbon showing the delicate details of their appearance. And even sandstone casts showing in remarkable detail the texture of dinosaur skin have been found in western Canada.

Fossils often preserve in remarkable detail the structure and texture of plants and animals such as the fossil fern at left, and the cast of dinosaur skin at right. Below is an ant beautifully preserved in amber, fossil resin of trees.

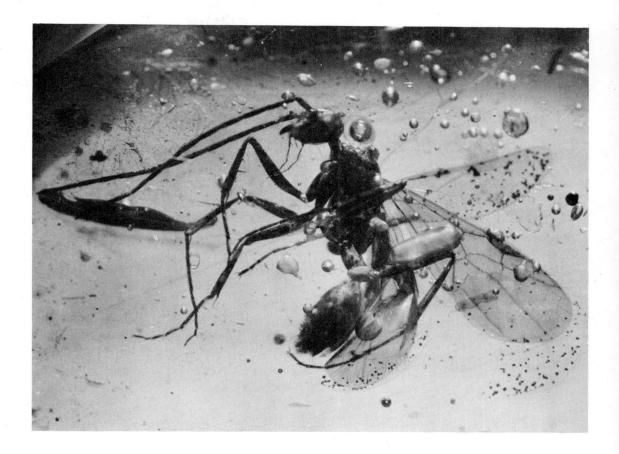

### How fossils are used

All of our knowledge of past life is based on fossils and the rocks in which they are found. Fossils tell us that all present-day plants and animals have primitive ancestors that lived on the Earth many millions of years ago. In most cases, the very old ancestral plants and animals were not able to go on living and reproducing themselves; they died out, or became **extinct**. All we know about the dinosaurs and other extinct organisms comes from a study of their fossil remains.

Fossils also tell us something about the position of seas and land masses of the past. Such animals as corals, brachiopods, and trilobites have lived only in the sea. By following the curving shoreline of an ancient inland sea now marked by rock containing marine fossils, we can trace the outline of that sea. Two thousand years ago the Greeks clearly saw in the fossil remains signs that land areas had sunk and risen at various times. (But others believed the fossils to be only the remains of some "ancient worker's lunch.") The trunks of fossil trees found where they originally grew tell us of a former land area. We then know that an ancient sea did not cover that area at the time the trees were growing.

Paleontologists can also find out about the climate of the past by studying fossils. What would you think if you found fossil tree ferns or fossil magnolias

What we know about the dinosaurs and the lands they roamed some 70 million years ago comes from a study of fossils. This famous mural at Yale's Peabody Museum of Natural History was painted by Rudolph F. Zallinger.

in Antarctica or Greenland? Such plants were actually found in those places. You would have to say that the climate there was indeed much warmer at that time, perhaps a tropical climate. Coal deposits often contain tree ferns and other plants. These plants suggest, again, a rather warm and swampy region during the time the coal deposits were forming. But today many of these coal deposits are found in parts of the world that are quite cold and dry. The climate had to be much different then from what it is today in those places in order for warm swamplands to have existed.

But we still have not talked about one of the most important uses of fossils. Fossils give us very important clues about the age of the rocks that contain them. Let us see how this was first discovered.

A study of fossils about 470 million years old leads geologists to think that much of North America was then covered by inland seas (color), as it has been for much of its geologic history.

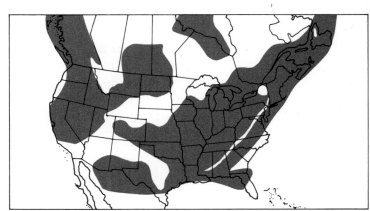

William Smith 1769–1839

During the seventeenth century, scientists knew for certain that the older rock strata are covered by younger ones. The arrangement of these layers in such an orderly sequence is known as the **law of superposition.** This law states that, in a normal sequence of strata, younger rocks are always found on top of older ones.

Around the year 1800, an English surveyor and civil engineer named William Smith learned that the success of different engineering projects—particularly the building of canals—depended on the kind of rock strata found in the region where the canal was to be dug. As he studied different rock layers, he saw that many of them had fossils. Soon he noticed that any single rock layer usually contained the same assemblage of fossils. The younger rock layers above, and the older rock layers below, each had different kinds of fossils. Soon, Smith became so skillful that whenever he saw a fossil he could tell from which layer of rock the fossil was collected.

At about the same time, two French geologists were studying and mapping the extent of the fossil-bearing strata that surround Paris. Both Georges Cuvier and Alexandre Brongniart also discovered that certain fossils were found only in certain rock layers. These two geologists also had used the law of super-position to arrange the rocks in the Paris area in chronological order, just as Smith had done in England. They, too, came to realize that each individual rock layer contained its own distinctive assemblage of fossils.

As Cuvier and Brongniart arranged their collections of fossils in the same order as the rocks from which they came, they discovered something else. They learned that the fossils changed in an orderly way from layer to layer. Cuvier and Brongniart compared the fossil forms with the more modern forms of life. It soon became evident that the fossils from the higher, and,

100

therefore, younger, rock layers were more similar to modern forms of life than those fossils from rock strata lower down.

By studying the fossil assemblage in any layer of sedimentary rock, scientists are able to tell the *relative* age of that rock layer. This fact has been proven time and again by other geologists and paleontologists throughout the world. Each rock layer usually contains its own distinctive fossil assemblage. But the rock layers above, and those below, contain different assemblages of fossils. Over the years following the work of Smith, Cuvier, and Brongniart, more and more information about the positions of fossils in the rock layers rapidly accumulated from all parts of the world. Today it is possible to place even a single kind of fossil from any part of the world into its proper time period.

When scientists discovered that fossils could help tell them the relative age of the rock that contained them, they were then able to start to unravel the complex history of our planet.

Fossils, then, tell us two important things: (1) that certain kinds of plants and animals were living together during certain time periods when certain sediments were forming; and (2) whether the sediments were formed on a shallow sea floor, in a desert, in a river bed, or in a swamp. By carefully studying fossils and the sedimentary rock that contains them, a paleontologist can learn a lot about the past. He can, bit by bit, build up the setting for a giant and extinct reptile such as *Brontosaurus*. He can tell what this dinosaur looked like, what animal neighbors it had, the plants that it ate, and he can picture the kinds of swamps in which it lived. Like a detective, the paleontologist puts together all of the clues he can find, and from them he recalls fascinating scenes of ancient worlds.

Fossils help geologists to tell which rock layers are missing and to compare their ages. Fossils (in diagram) are numbered 1 to 5, with 1 the oldest.

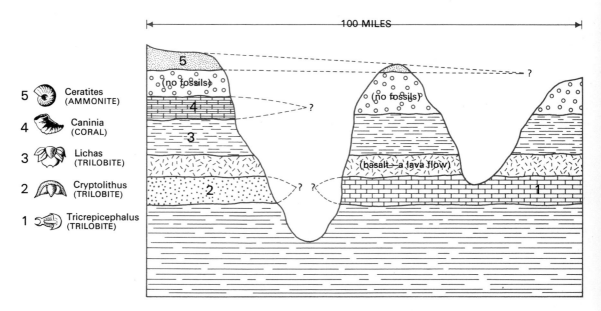

These eroded hills, revealing their layered sediments in Alberta, Canada, are reminders of the vast span of geologic time, of the centuries melting into millennia. Its passage is so slow that our minds cannot begin to grasp it.

# 9   Telling Geologic Time

Fossils had been forming long, long before the time when the great glacier covering much of North America, Europe, and Asia began to melt away about 10,000 years ago. But the question "How much longer?" was not an easy one to answer. Much research and many careful studies had to be carried out before geologists could work out a scale of time. The work of Smith, Cuvier, and others clearly showed that some fossils were older than others. But the question that troubled these men was "*exactly* how old was a given fossil—ten thousand, ten million, or ten hundred million years old?"

Geologists soon learned that many events in the history of the Earth must have taken vast lengths of time. How long would it take for a river to form a valley, or a volcano to build a 5000-foot cone? How long would it take for mountains such as the Rockies in North America, or the Himalayas in Asia, to form? So vast is the span of time of the Earth's history that our minds

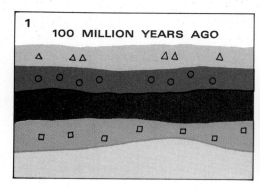

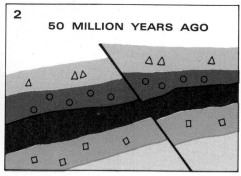

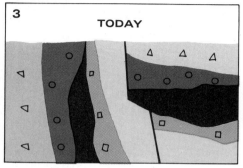

The geologic record is often confused by upheavals that twist the rock layers out of order (diagrams 2 and 3). Because the same kinds of fossils (circles, triangles, and squares) are often found in similar rock layers, fossils are valuable clues that help geologists unscramble the rock record.

cannot easily imagine its length. To separate this kind of time from our own limited idea of time (an hour, a day, a century), we use the term **geologic time**. Geologic time represents thousands and millions of years in the history of the Earth.

### Relative and absolute geologic time

One way of looking at time is to ask if one event happened before or after another event. We speak of this "before" or "after" time as **relative** geologic time. Relative time does not involve years. For example, did the Revolutionary War come before or after the Civil War? You may know that the Revolutionary War came first, but knowing the year when it began is quite another matter.

When we study the history of the Earth, we want to know if the Rockies were formed before or after the Appalachians—but we also would like to know *exactly*, in the number of years, when these different events occurred. As soon as we know the date an event took place, we are then dealing with **absolute** geologic time. Returning to our example of American wars, we express *relative* time by saying that the Revolutionary War took place before the Civil War; but we express *absolute* time by saying that the Revolutionary War began in the year 1775 and that the Civil War began in the year 1861.

Geologic time works in the same two ways. First, we can think of geologic time in a relative way. We want to know if some event, such as a volcanic eruption, came before or after another event, such as the advance of a glacier. We also would like to know the date of each event. Only after we know when one event happened relative to another, can we begin to reconstruct the *order* in which the events happened in the very long history of the Earth. Then, absolute time tells us in numbers of years when any geologic event happened.

The fossils collected by paleontologists help geologists date the layer of sedimentary rock in which the fossils are found.

### The geological time scale

You have already learned two very important facts about the history of the
Earth. First, in a normal arrangement of sedimentary strata, younger rocks
are always on top of older rocks. Second, the relative age of a rock layer can
often be told by the fossils it contains. Each layer of sedimentary rock has its
own distinctive group of fossils.

Unfortunately we know of no single place on the land surface of the Earth
where all the "pages of the Earth's diary," or the rock record, are preserved
intact exactly as they were formed. In one land area much of the record may
be missing, having been eroded away mostly by streams and rivers. In another
area, many of the sedimentary strata may have been changed so much by
great Earth pressures that we can barely read their history. In addition, the
rocks of the Earth's crust are often twisted, folded, broken or disfigured in
other ways. The geologist's problem is to unscramble the bits and pieces, know
what pieces are missing, then rearrange the puzzle so that its story can be read.

His most important tool for making the puzzle readable are the fossils
that occur in sedimentary rock strata the world over. A certain kind of mammal fossil, say, is likely to be found only in rocks of a certain age. Suppose
that a geologist in England finds those particular mammal fossils in a layer
of rock exposed to the air. Suppose, also, that a geologist examining a rock
layer many feet beneath the ground in Wyoming finds the same kinds of
mammal fossils. By comparing their fossils, the two geologists know that the
sedimentary rocks each is studying are about the same age. On the other
hand, if the English geologist's rock sample contains fossils of mammals
known to have lived earlier, then he knows that his rock is older than the
Wyoming rock sample—even though the two rock samples may be exactly
alike in every other respect. In this way, the geologist can arrange fossil-

bearing rock strata from all over the world in their proper time sequence. If a part of the rock record is missing in one area, he can find the missing record somewhere else. He then places this part of the record from the one area in its proper position with the rocks in the other place.

Thus, geologists imagine the rock layers that have been laid down since the beginning of Earth time as forming a continuous column of rock containing a rather complete geologic history of the Earth. The period of time when the youngest rock formed is at the top of the rock column, and the oldest time periods are at the bottom.

Most of the early work in arranging fossil-bearing rocks in a time sequence was done in Britain and Western Europe. Therefore, most of the names used in the geologic time table are taken from places in Europe. The geologic time chart on pages 111 to 114 shows the various geologic periods in their proper time sequence. It also shows a few of the different kinds of fossils found in rocks formed at different times, and it gives the approximate time, in years, when the rock layers were being formed. So far, although we have mentioned absolute geologic time, we have not explained how geologists are able to tell that a certain piece of rock is, say, 250 million years old.

### Atomic clocks—measuring absolute time

In 1896 the French physicist Antoine Henri Becquerel discovered **radioactivity**—a natural process in which certain elements change themselves into different elements. They do this as the central portions, or **nuclei**, of their atoms break down. With this discovery, a new chapter in the story of telling

**MEASURING THE HALF-LIFE OF A RADIO-ACTIVE ELEMENT**
( See text on opposite page )

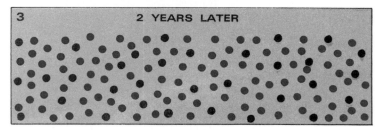

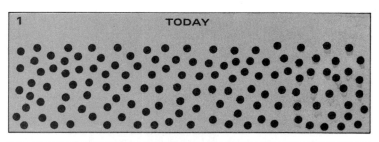

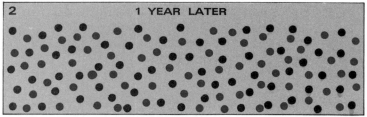

geologic time was written. It meant that geologists had "atomic clocks" which could measure quite exactly when certain events occurred in the Earth's very long history. Let us see how these atomic clocks work.

Imagine that you have a large box with 12,800 black marbles in it (diagram 1). You want to find out how old the boxful of marbles is. Imagine also that the black marbles "age" by turning brown. In one year, half of the black marbles turn brown (diagram 2). At the end of the first year, there would be 6400 black marbles left, and 6400 brown ones. At the end of the second year, half of the remaining 6400 black marbles turn brown (diagram 3). There would then be 3200 black and 9600 brown marbles. This process would go on and on until our clock "ran down," so to speak.

## TELLING THE PASSAGE OF TIME WITH BLACK MARBLES CHANGING TO BROWN

| Passage of time in years | Number of black marbles | Number of brown marbles | Black-brown ratio |
|---|---|---|---|
| 0 | 12,800 | 0 | 0 |
| 1 | 6,400 | 6,400 | 1:1 |
| 2 | 3,200 | 9,600 | 1:3 |
| 3 | 1,600 | 11,200 | 1:7 |
| 4 | 800 | 12,000 | 1:15 |
| 5 | 400 | 12,400 | 1:31 |
| 6 | 200 | 12,600 | 1:63 |
| 7 | 100 | 12,700 | 1:127 |
| 8 | 50 | 12,750 | 1:255 |
| 9 | 25 | 12,775 | 1:511 |

If you counted 800 black marbles and 12,000 brown ones, you would know that four years had gone by since the first black marble turned brown. But can you think of an easier way to tell how much time went by without counting *all* of the marbles?

Simply scoop a jarful of marbles—maybe 1000—out of the box, then count how many brown and black ones you have in the sample. Then divide the number of black ones into the number of brown ones. This is the black-brown ratio (see right-hand column of table). In your sample of 1000 marbles, there would be 61 black ones and 939 brown ones if the box were four years old, giving a ratio of 1:15.

Very simply, that is how a radioactive clock works. The scientist measures the ratio between the number of unchanged atoms of a radioactive element, and the number of new atoms that have formed. The amount of time needed for half of the atoms of a radioactive element to change is called its **half-life.** Nothing seems to affect the half-life of any radioactive element—neither changes in temperature nor changes in pressure. Since the scientist knows the half-life of the radioactive element, and since he can measure the ratio of the numbers of new and old atoms, he can then tell how long the "clock has been running."

Different radioactive elements have different half-lives. Here are three different radioactive elements that are used to tell the absolute age of rocks, the elements they change into, and their half-life.

| This radioactive element... | | changes into... | and has a half-life of... |
|---|---|---|---|
| uranium 238 | → | lead 206 | 4510 million years |
| potassium 40 | → | argon 40 | 1350 million years |
| rubidium 40 | → | strontium 87 | 6 million years |

Since radioactive potassium 40 is found in several common and widespread minerals—such as feldspar and mica—it may one day become the most popular method in finding out the absolute age of rocks.

Let us see now how geologists go about reading absolute time in rocks. The diagrams on this page show the long history of rock formation in a part

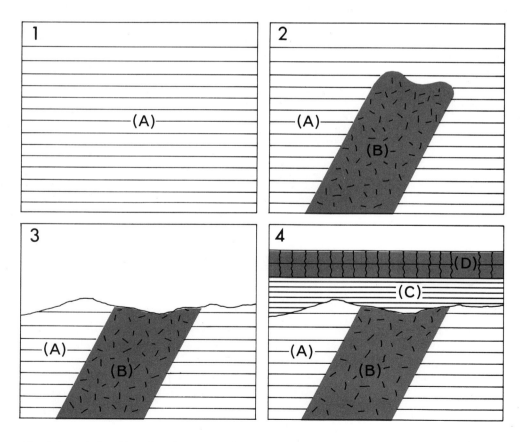

By determining the absolute age of igneous rocks, the maximum and minimum absolute age of sedimentary rocks can be found. (Text explains diagram.)

of the Earth's crust. In the first diagram, sediments (A) were formed by being deposited one on top of the other. Soon they became hard, coherent sedimentary rock strata. Later, magma formed an intrusive granite dike (B) in the sedimentary strata. This was followed by a long period of erosion which exposed the dike. Finally, in diagram 4, more sediments (C) were laid down, with a lava flow (D) at the top.

From the "law of superposition," we know that the *relative* ages are (A), (B), (C), and (D), (A) being the oldest rocks. Say that we find fossils in the sedimentary strata (A) and know the fossils to be of Jurassic age. We also know that fossils in the (C) sediments are of Middle Tertiary age. From a sample of feldspar, the potassium-argon ratio shows an age of 90 million years for the granite dike. From a sample of a mineral in the lava (D) we get an absolute age of 15 million years, also by using the potassium-argon method.

Rocks of Jurassic age, then, must be older than 90 million years. More information from another area might then tell us exactly how much older they are. And since the lava flow is closely related to the sedimentary strata (C), rocks of Middle Tertiary age are about 15 million years old. But to find out *just* how much older, we would have to turn to other sources where similar rocks occur.

Unfortunately, radioactive minerals suitable for dating geologic events come mostly from igneous rocks; it is hard to get a reliable absolute age directly from sedimentary rocks. By using the radioactive dates from igneous rocks, scientists have been able to say that the Jurassic, Permian, and other divisions of relative geologic time are so and so many millions of years old.

As our knowledge about the rocks and fossils of the Earth grows year by year, we often have to change our ideas about the times when certain geologic events took place. For example, in 1961 geologists established that the Silurian Period began 425 million years ago and ended 405 million years ago. In the light of new evidence, these figures were changed in 1964 to a beginning date of 440 million years and a closing date of 395 million years. As a result of this change, the time span of the Silurian Period was doubled. Also in 1961, the Pleistocene Epoch had a beginning date of one million years ago. But in 1964 this figure was revised to 1.7 million years. Here again, the span of geologic time included in the Pleistocene Epoch was nearly doubled. As the instruments used to measure the age of minerals become more accurate, absolute dates in our geologic calendar will continue to be revised.

Usually, only very small amounts of a radioactive material are present in a rock being studied. This means that the slightest error in measurement may mean a large error in the ratio between the two elements. It would be like taking a sample of only 10 marbles, rather than 1000. The point is that a sample of 1000 will be more representative of the total of the blacks and browns among 12,800 marbles than would a sample of only 10 marbles. A slight error in measurement of a small radioactive sample may mean a difference of millions of years in the final absolute age figure. Just a 5-per cent error in a 100-million-year-old rock might mean an error of 5 million years. This would be just a little less than three times the age of all humanity itself!

## Backward into time

If you have read this book through from the beginning, you now have some idea of the revealing stories a rock can tell. Learning to read the stories, however, takes time, patience, and a lot of effort, but so does anything else that you learn to do well.

Sedimentary rock strata are stone "pages" which, when opened layer by layer, reveal the geologic history of a region over periods of hundreds of millions of years. In a way, you hold time in the palm of your hand when you hold a many-layered piece of sedimentary rock, or when you hold any rock for that matter. But the sedimentary rocks are, perhaps, the most fascinating, not only for their variety in color and form, but especially for their fossils. The succession of life forms as they have evolved on this planet is revealed to us when we open the pages of sedimentary rocks.

At this moment, on my desk is a small rock containing beautifully preserved fossil ammonites, snail-like sea animals that lived long, long ago and which are now extinct. Because the rock shows a certain variety of the animals, I know that it is about 170 million years old. Each time I pick it up to admire nature's work in so beautifully preserving these sea creatures, I have a sense of being linked with the past, with a time long, long before man appeared on the Earth. Other rocks in my collection are older still, and others more recent. Knowing how, when, and where they were formed, and the stories they have to tell, makes me rich in a small but important way.

If you intend to start a rock collection, don't rush into it. Select your specimens with care, and study them with care. When you do, you will unlock and discover many fascinating stories revealed by the Earth's treasure of rocks and minerals.

Archaeopteryx, the first known bird from the fossil record, was discovered in a quarry in Solenhofen, Bavaria. Its length is about eighteen inches and it occurred in limestone of the Late Jurassic Period (about 140 million years ago).

# The Ages of the Earth

## A GEOLOGICAL TIME CHART

Shown on the following pages is the geological time scale for the history of the Earth which has been worked out by scientists who study rocks and fossils. While the "Period" is the most important division in this time scale, the different periods are grouped together under the larger division called the "Era." Note that most of the names given to the periods are place names for localities where rocks of that age were first studied and described. On the other hand, Tertiary (meaning "third") and Quaternary (meaning "fourth") are names retained from an earlier fourfold division of the rocks.

The purpose of this geologic calendar is to give you an idea when a few of the major events in the geological history of our planet occurred.

| ERA | PERIOD | | THE LAND | THE SEA | LIVING THINGS |
|---|---|---|---|---|---|
| CENOZOIC (from the Greek words kainos meaning "recent" and zoe meaning "life") | QUATERNARY (meaning "fourth") Present to 1.7 millions years ago | RECENT EPOCH / PLEISTOCENE EPOCH | The Cascadian Disturbance deformed the Coast Ranges of the west coast of North America and caused widespread volcanic activity. This disturbance is probably still going on today. | Continental glaciers developed on the continents of North America, northern Europe, and Antarctica while valley glaciers formed in the high mountain regions. There were four glacial and three interglacial ages. The heights of the sea varied with the formation and melting of ice. | Modern horses and oxen appeared at the beginning of this period. Of the several man-like animals that developed, only one species (Homo sapiens) survived and occurs in great numbers today. |
| | TERTIARY (meaning "third") 1.7 million to 65 million years ago | | There was widespread volcanic activity in the western United States. Mounts Shasta and Rainier were formed, as was the great Alpine-Himalayan mountain chain. There was also volcanic activity in the North Atlantic region, in East Africa, and in the Mediterranean region. | Most of the inland seas left the continents, and by the end of this period the continents had the same general outlines that they have today. | Grasslands became widespread. Mammals became the dominant land animals. By this time cats, monkeys, whales, elephants, kangaroos, and birds were well established. |
| MESOZOIC (from the Greek words mesos meaning "middle" and zoe meaning "life") | CRETACEOUS (from the Latin word creta, meaning "chalk") 65 million to 136 million years ago | | The Rocky Mountains of North America and the Andes of South America were formed as a result of the Laramide Disturbance. | Cretaceous seas covered most of Europe, much of Asia, and nearly half of North America. The Gulf of Mexico received nearly 11,000 feet of sediments during this period. | Flowering plants were common, the giant sequoias had also become common. Sharks again became abundant. Snakes make their first appearance. It was during this period that the last of the dinosaurs disappeared from the face of the land. |
| | JURASSIC (named after the Jura Mountains) 136 million to 195 million years ago | | A period of relative quiet. The Sierra Nevada Mountains were formed. Geosyncline downsinking took place along the western edges of both North and South America. In a way, the Jurassic was a stage-setting period for the great activity during the Cretaceous Period. | Jurassic seas changed little from the Triassic (see below). Seas continued to cover the western borders of North and South America. | Among plants, cycads, ferns and scouring rushes flourished, and the first true pine trees appeared. Dinosaurs became numerous. The first lizards arose. Pterodactyls and feathered birds also appeared as did small mammals. Plesiosaurs, marine reptiles, became quite huge, measuring some 20 feet in length. |

## TRIASSIC

*(from the Latin word trias, meaning three and referring to a threefold division of rock in southern Germany)*

195 million to 225 million years ago

Extensive igneous activity took place during the Triassic, which includes the formation of the famous Palisades of New York-New Jersey, and similar rocks in South America, southern Africa, Australia, and Antarctica.

Seaways continued to cover the western edges of North and South America, and some parts of Europe and Asia.

Due to cooler seas, or for some other reason, many marine creatures such as sharks did poorly during this period. Thecodonts, ancestors of the dinosaurs, arose, as did turtles. Crocodiles also made their appearance along with marine reptiles such as ichthyosaurs.

## PALEOZOIC

*(from the Greek words palaios meaning "ancient" and zoe meaning "life")*

### PERMIAN

*(named after the Province of Perm in the Ural Mountains of Russia)*

225 million to 280 million years ago

The Appalachians south of New England were formed from the Appalachian Geosyncline. The Ural Mountains were also formed. Along the west coast of North America there was widespread volcanic activity. The reddish sedimentary strata of Monument Valley, Utah, were laid down during this time.

The western United States was still covered by shallow seas during this period. In other parts of the Northern Hemisphere seas were drying up and leaving vast deposits of salt and potash.

Conifers increased, while the giant scouring rushes died out. Trilobites, some corals, and some amphibians also became extinct. A generally drying climate caused many plant and animal species to die out, but favored the success of reptiles. Numerous varieties of reptiles have been discovered from this period.

### PENNSYLVANIAN

*(named after the coal regions of Pennsylvania)*

280 million to 310 million years ago

The Ouachita Mountains (see below) were altered many times during this period. Uplifting of the sea beds in the Northern Hemisphere produced new low-lying land. In the Southern Hemisphere there was widespread glaciation.

Some areas of the land sank, giving rise to vast lakes, swamps and brackish lagoons, but in general the inland shallow seas of the Northern Hemisphere were not so widespread as they were during the Mississippian.

About half of the world's workable coal was formed during this period, mainly from giant scale trees. Amphibians, some of them 15 feet or so long and resembling salamanders, ruled the land. The first reptiles arose during this period. Conifers (cone-bearing trees) and 40-foot-high scouring rushes were common.

### MISSISSIPPIAN

*(named after the limestone area near the junction of the Mississippi and Missouri Rivers)*

310 million to 345 million years ago

The Variscan Disturbance raised extensive mountains in western Europe. The Ouachita Mountains of Oklahoma and Arkansas were formed.

Clear, shallow seas were still widespread in the Northern Hemisphere. The Appalachian Geosyncline, formed during the Cambrian Period, collected extensive deposits of sandy and muddy sediments from the rivers flowing down from the eastern land mass. Limestone was the most common sediment deposited in the shallow seas covering the mid-continent region.

Sharks were abundant during this period, and amphibians made their appearance as the major land animal. Hundred-foot-high scale trees grew on the edges of pools, shallow lakes, and swamps. Winged insects appeared for the first time, one with a wing-span of 29 inches (*Meganeura*).

| ERA | PERIOD | THE LAND | THE SEA | LIVING THINGS |
|---|---|---|---|---|
| PALEOZOIC (continued) | DEVONIAN (named after Devon, England) 345 million to 395 million years ago | A land disturbance (called the Acadian Disturbance) raised high mountains in New England, Quebec, and Nova Scotia. The Kanimbla Disturbance raised mountains along the east coast of Australia. | Most of North America continued to be covered by shallow seas during most of the Devonian. | The Devonian is the "Age of Fishes." A bewildering variety of fishes arose during this period. Plants were plentiful and included giant tree ferns 40 feet tall. Late in this period lobe-finned fishes began to establish themselves on the land. |
| | SILURIAN (named after the Silures, an ancient tribe living in Wales) 395 million to 440 million years ago | There was much volcanic activity in Maine, New Brunswick, and eastern Quebec. Land disturbances (called the Caledonian Disturbance) gave rise to a 4000-mile-long mountain range extending from Wales through Scandinavia and westward to northern Greenland. | Most of the present-day land area of the Northern Hemisphere was under water during this period. Extensive salt deposits, such as those of western New York and Michigan, were formed. | The trilobites began to decrease in numbers during this period. Eurypterids, or "water scorpions," were quite common. The first land plants—ferns and psilopsids—appeared. |
| | ORDOVICIAN (named after an ancient Celtic tribe, the Ordovices, living in Wales) 440 million to 500 million years ago | Late during the Ordovician Period the crust of the Earth extending from Newfoundland to the Carolinas of the United States was affected by granitic intrusions, metamorphism, and folding, and giving rise to mountains of this Taconic Disturbance. | About 70 per cent of the present-day Northern Hemisphere was flooded during this period. | This was a rich period for marine life. Trilobites were numerous, as were bryozoans, graptolites, cephalopods, and crinoids. Jawless fishes also arose. |
| | CAMBRIAN (Roman name for Wales) 500 million to 570 million years ago | In North America, Europe, and Asia great troughs in the land (called "geosynclines") were filling up with sediments. Near the end of the Paleozoic Era, this sedimentary "fill" was thrust up as mountain ranges. The Rocky Mountain and Appalachian Geosynclines formed during this period. | Sometime during this era the seas formed. But these early seas and oceans did not have the shape of our seas and oceans of today. | The shallow Cambrian seas abounded with many forms of life, including sponges, trilobites, brachiopods, graptolites, and other animals without backbones. |
| PRECAMBRIAN 570 million to 4500 million years ago | | The Sun and Planets were formed. The Earth, which may have been a molten sphere, developed a hard crust. Sedimentary rocks of this age are rare. Most have been metamorphosed by heat and pressure during the later periods so that their record is difficult to decipher. | Sometime during this era the seas formed. But these early seas and oceans did not have the shape of our seas and oceans of today. | The first living things may have come into being about 3000 million years ago. Rare fossils of algae-like and fungi-like plants have been discovered. Fossil imprints of jelly-fishes, worm burrows, and, recently, brachiopods have also been found. |

A specimen of hornblende schist, a regional metamorphic rock, with a layer of quartz, from New York City.

 Where To Find It

### Books, Pamphlets, and Magazines About Rocks, Minerals, and Fossils

You will find the following pages very useful in your search for detailed information about rocks, minerals, and fossils.

Listed under Group A are many offices and organizations that will send you information about geology. If you write to any of them, *don't* ask them to send you "all the information you have about geology." Tell them exactly what kind of information you want; for example, radioactive minerals in a certain state, or the chief sources of a certain ore in the United States. Before you go exploring in any part of the United States, Canada, or Mexico and Central America, get as much information as you can beforehand. The publications of the United States Geological Survey and those of the geological surveys of the individual states will be of greatest value to you.

Listed under Group B are some books and other publications dealing with geology. Those that are marked with an asterisk (*) are the ones we think you might find most useful. Those that are marked (A) are more advanced than those marked (I), for intermediate.

Listed under Group C are a few books and pamphlets that describe specific collecting areas and provide detailed directions and maps showing how to get there. These will help you find new places to explore for rocks, minerals, and fossils. Others include the rock and mineral resources of an individual state.

Listed under Group D are some magazines that you may find interesting to read and might want to subscribe to.

## GROUP A

### UNITED STATES

**U.S. Geological Survey,** U.S. Department of the Interior, Washington 25, D.C.
(Issues a general catalog of its publications—see Group B. Geologic maps for sale by the U.S. Geological Survey are listed in its general catalog of publications. They offer a free Index Circular of topographic maps. The individual topographic maps may be purchased by mail as follows:
Maps and the Index Circular of topographic maps covering areas in the United States west of the Mississippi River and including all of Louisiana and Minnesota may be ordered from the U.S. Geological Survey, Federal Center, Denver, Colorado. Topographic maps and Index Circulars for areas east of the Mississippi should be ordered from the U.S. Geological Survey, Washington 25, D.C.)

**U.S. Government Printing Office,** Washington 25, D.C.
(Practically all publications about geology and related subjects prepared by the various agencies of the U.S. government are sold by this office. Lists of a large variety of subjects are mailed free upon request.)

STATE GEOLOGICAL SURVEYS

**Alaska** Geological Survey, Alaska Branch, Brooks Memorial Building, P.O. Box 4004, College.
Geological Survey, Alaskan Distribution Unit (publications), 520 Illinois Street, Fairbanks.
Bureau of Mines, Juneau Experiment Station (mineral identifications).

**Alabama** Bureau of Mines, Southern Experiment Station, Box 1, Tuscaloosa (mineral identifications).
Geological Survey of Alabama, Smith Hall, University of Alabama, University.

**Arizona** Geological Survey, Mineral Deposits Branch, University of Arizona, University Station, Tucson.
Bureau of Mines, Southwest Experiment Station, University of Arizona, University Station, Tucson (mineral identifications).
Arizona Bureau of Mines, University of Arizona, Tucson.

**Arkansas** Division of Geology, Arkansas Geological and Conservation Commission, State Capitol, Little Rock.

**California** Geological Survey, Mineral Deposits Branch, Geologic Division, 116 North Alexander, Claremont.

Geological Survey, Public Inquiries Office, 807 Post Office and Courthouse Building, Los Angeles 12.

California State Division of Mines, Department of Natural Resources, Ferry Building, San Francisco 11 (publish many books, maps, etc., on all phases of California mines, mining and geology).

**Colorado** Geological Survey, Mineral Deposits Branch, Geologic Division, P.O. Box 360, Grand Junction.

Geological Survey, Public Inquiries Office, 468 New Customs Building, Denver 2.

Bureau of Mines, Denver Experiment Station, Denver Federal Center, Colorado Commissioner of Mines, State Museum Building, Denver.

**Connecticut** Connecticut Geological and Natural History Survey, University of Connecticut, Storrs.

**Delaware** Delaware Geological Survey, Department of Geography & Geology, University of Delaware, Newark.

**Florida** Florida Geological Survey, P.O. Drawer 631, Tallahassee.

**Georgia** Georgia Department of Mines, Mining and Geology, 19 Hunter Street, S.W., Atlanta 3.

**Hawaii** Geological Survey, Geologist in Charge, Hawaiian Volcano Observatory, Hawaiian National Park.

**Idaho** Idaho Bureau of Mines and Geology, University of Idaho, Moscow.

**Illinois** Illinois State Geological Survey, 100 Natural Resources Building, Urbana.

**Indiana** Geological Survey, Indiana Department of Conservation, Indiana University, Bloomington.

**Iowa** Iowa Geological Survey, Geology Annex, Iowa City.

**Kansas** Kansas State Geological Survey, University of Kansas, Lawrence.

**Kentucky** Kentucky Geological Survey, University of Kentucky, Lexington.

**Louisiana** Louisiana Geological Survey, Geology Building, Louisiana State University, Baton Rouge 3.

**Maine** Maine Department of Economic Development, Division of Geologic Survey, State House, Augusta.

**Maryland** Maryland Department of Geology, Mines and Water Resources, Johns Hopkins University, Baltimore 18.

**Massachusetts** Locations & Surveys Engineer, Highways Division, Massachusetts Department of Public Works, 100 Nashua Street, Boston.

**Michigan** Geological Survey Division, Michigan Department of Conservation, Lansing 26.

**Minnesota** Bureau of Mines, North Central Experiment Station, 2908 Colfax Avenue South, Minneapolis 8 (mineral identifications).

Minnesota Geological Survey, University of Minnesota, Minneapolis 11.

**Missouri** Bureau of Mines, Mississippi Valley Experiment Station, P.O. Box 136, Rolla (mineral identification).

Missouri Division of Geological Survey and Water Resources, P.O. Box 250, Rolla.

**Montana** Geological Survey, Regional Mining Supervisor, 323 Federal Building, Billings.

Montana Bureau of Mines and Geology, Montana School of Mines, Butte.

**Nebraska** Nebraska Conservation and Survey Division, University of Nebraska, Lincoln 8.

**Nevada** Bureau of Mines, Rare and Precious Metals Experiment Station, 1605 Evans Avenue, Reno (mineral identifications).

Nevada Bureau of Mines, University of Nevada, Reno.

**New Hampshire** New Hampshire State Planning and Development Commission, Conant Hall, Durham.

**New Jersey** Bureau of Geology and Topography, New Jersey Department of Conservation and Economic Development, 520 E. State Street, Trenton 7.

**New Mexico** New Mexico Bureau of Mines and Mineral Resources, Camous Station, Socorro.

**New York** New York Geological and Natural History Surveys, State Education Building, Albany 1.

**North Carolina** Division of Mineral Resources, North Carolina Department of Conservation and Development, Box 2719, 253 Education Building, Raleigh.

**North Dakota** North Dakota Geological Survey, University Station, Grand Forks.

**Ohio** Ohio Department of Natural Resources, Division of Geological Survey, Orton Hall, Ohio State University, Columbus 10.

Oklahoma Geological Survey, Regional Mining Supervisor, 205 Federal Building, Miami.

Oklahoma Geological Survey, University of Oklahoma, Norman.

Oregon Geological Survey Office, Interior Building, 1001 N.E. Lloyd Boulevard, Portland 14.

Bureau of Mines, Northwest Electrodevelopment Experiment Station, P.O. Box 492, Albany (mineral identifications).

Oregon Department of Geology and Mineral Industries, 1065 State Office Building, Portland.

Pennsylvania Bureau of Topographic and Geological Survey, Pennsylvania Department of Internal Affairs, Harrisburg.

Rhode Island Rhode Island Development Council, 320 State House, Providence.

Mineral Resources Committee, Department of Geology, Brown Univ., Providence.

South Carolina South Carolina Geological Survey, University of South Carolina, Columbia 19.

South Dakota Bureau of Mines, Rapid City Experiment Station, School of Mines Campus, Rapid City (mineral identifications).

South Dakota State Geological Survey, Union Building, State University, Vermillion.

Tennessee Geological Survey, Mineral Deposits Branch, 13 Post Office Building, Knoxville 1.

Tennessee State Department of Conservation, Division of Geology, G-5 State Office Building, Nashville 3.

Texas Bureau of Economic Geology, Univ. of Texas, University Station, Box 8022, Austin 12.

Utah Geological Survey, Regional Geologist, 506 Federal Building, Salt Lake City 1.

Geological Survey, Public Inquiries Office, 504 Federal Building, Salt Lake City 1 (publications and maps sold).

Geological Survey, Mineral Deposits Branch, 222 S.W. Temple, Salt Lake City 1.

Bureau of Mines, Intermountain Experiment Station, 1600 East First Street, South, Salt Lake City (mineral identifications).

Utah Geological and Mineralogical Survey, University of Utah, Rm. 200, Mines Building, Salt Lake City 12.

Vermont Vermont Geological Survey, East Hall, University of Vermont, Burlington.

Washington Geological Survey, Mineral Deposits Branch, South 157 Howard Street, Spokane 8.

Washington State Division of Mines and Geology, 335 General Administration Building, Olympia.

West Virginia West Virginia Geological and Economic Survey, P.O. Box 879, Mineral Industries Building, Morgantown.

Wisconsin Geological Survey, Mineral Deposits Branch, Department of Geology, University of Wisconsin, Science Hall, Madison 6.

Wyoming Geological Survey of Wyoming, University of Wyoming, Laramie.

## CANADA

Canada Department of Mines & Technical Surveys, Ottawa, Ontario: Surveys and Mapping Branch (map distribution offices). Geological Survey of Canada (publications). Mines Branch (publications).

Alberta Geological Survey of Canada, Western Office, 406 Customs Building, Calgary.

British Columbia Geological Survey of Canada, Branch Office, 739 W. Hastings Street, Vancouver 1.

British Columbia Department of Mines, Victoria.

Manitoba Manitoba Department of Mines and Natural Resources, Winnipeg; includes a Lands Branch, Surveys Branch, and Mines Branch.

New Brunswick New Brunswick Department of Lands and Mines, Fredericton.

Newfoundland Newfoundland Department of Mines and Resources, St. John's; the Mines Branch includes: The Geological Survey of Newfoundland, Crown Lands and Surveys Division, and the Mining Division.

Northwest Territories Geological Survey of Canada, Branch Office, Yellowknife.

Department of Northern Affairs and National Resources Office, Hay River.

Nova Scotia Nova Scotia Department of Mines, Provincial Building, Halifax.

Ontario Department of Mines and Technical Surveys, Ottawa.

Department of Northern Affairs and National Resources, Ottawa.

Ontario Department of Mines, Parliament

Buildings, Toronto; includes a Mining Lands Branch and a Geological Branch.

**Prince Edward Island**  Deputy Provincial Secretary, Provincial Government Offices, Charlottetown.

**Quebec**  Quebec Department of Mines, Quebec.

**Saskatchewan**  Saskatchewan Department of Mineral Resources, Administration Building, Regina; includes the Saskatchewan Geological Survey, Natural Resources Building, Regina.

**Yukon Territory**  Geological Survey of Canada, Branch Office, Whitehorse.

## MEXICO AND CENTRAL AMERICA

**Mexico**  Instituto de Geología, Universidad Nacional Autónoma de México, Cypres 176, México, D.F.

**Guatemala**  Facultad de Ingeniera, Universidad, San Carlos.

**British Honduras**  Survey Department, Belize.

**Nicaragua**  Servicio Geológico Nacional, Ministerio de Economía, Apartado Postal Numero 1347, Managua, D.N.

**El Salvador**  Servicio Geológico Nacional, Apartado Postal Numero 109, San Salvador.

**Costa Rica**  Sección Geología, Museo Nacional, Apartado Numero 749, San José.

## GROUP B

### PUBLICATIONS ABOUT GEOLOGY

*Directory of Geological Material in North America,* J. V. Howell and A. I. Levorsen, American Geological Institute, Washington 25, D.C.; 1957. A list of books and pamphlets, maps, photographs, and other material of use to the geologist and rock and mineral collector.

*Earth for the Layman,* M. W. Pangborn, American Geological Institute Report 2, Washington, D.C.; 1957. Over 1400 popular books and pamphlets on geology, mining, and other earth science subjects are listed.

*Field Guide to Rocks and Minerals,* F. H. Pough, Houghton Mifflin; 1955. One of the finest references available to the collector—a must for your library. All of the common minerals and rocks are described in detail. In addition, the different chemical tests are discussed together with the crystal classifications of minerals. (A)

*Fossils—A Guide to Prehistoric Life,* Golden Press; 1962. An excellent booklet with outstanding illustrations describing the different plants and animals that make up the fossil record. (I)

*Fossils—An Introduction to Prehistoric Life,* W. H. Matthews III, Barnes & Noble; 1962. An excellent and inexpensive paperback book that describes all aspects of paleontology, including collecting fossils, and the different plants and animals that lived during the various periods of geologic time.

*Getting Acquainted with Minerals,* G. L. English and D. E. Jensen, McGraw-Hill; 1959. A book with many illustrations that will help you learn more about minerals. (A)

*Literature of Geology, The,* B. Mason, The American Museum of Natural History, New York; 1953. A guide to bibliographies, dictionaries, directories, and other sources of geological information.

*Minerals and How to Study Them,* E. S. Dana and C. S. Hurlbut, John Wiley; Revised Edition; 1949. A book that will help you learn more about minerals. (A)

*Publications of the Geological Survey of Canada (1917–1952),* L. B. Leafloor, Department of Mines and Technical Surveys, Geological Survey of Canada; 1952. A catalog of the publications of the Geological Survey of Canada.

*Publications of the Geological Survey, with Supplements,* U.S. Geological Survey, Washington 25, D.C. The latest edition is May 1958. This is a complete catalog of all of the publications (including geologic and topographic maps) of the United States Geological Survey.

*Rock Book, The,* C. L. and M. A. Fenton, Doubleday; 1940. A popular and well-illustrated book describing the rocks of the Earth's crust. (A)

*Rockhound Buyer's Guide, The,* Lapidary Journal, P. O. Box 2369, San Diego, Calif. 92112. This book tells you where you can find dealers in rocks and minerals, rock and mineral clubs, and what field trips are offered. It is brought up to date each year.

119

*Rocks and Minerals, Golden Press; 1957. Most of the common rocks and minerals are described in adequate detail, together with some of the chemical methods used to identify them. Many excellent illustrations. Every collector should buy this booklet before getting Pough's *Field Guide to Rocks and Minerals.* (I)

Story of Geology, The, J. Wyckoff, Golden Press; 1960. A colorful book describing the various processes that operate on and within the Earth and that constantly change it. Many illustrations in color. (I)

World We Live In, The, L. Barnett, Time, Inc.; 1956. A colorful and rather complete book that discusses the formation, history, and fossil record of the Earth. (A)

Your Changing Earth, H. Ruchlis, Harvey; 1963. This book describes the origin of the Earth, its mountain systems, and the changes in its landscapes. (I)

## GROUP C

### SPECIAL COLLECTING AREAS

Agate Book, The, H. C. Dake, Gemac. (See end of listing for address.)

Arizona Gem Fields, A. Duke, Gemac.

Arizona Gem Trails and the Colorado Desert of California, J. E. Ransom, Gemac.

Arizona Rock Trails, Bitner, Gemac.

California Gem Trails, H. C. Dake, Gemac.

California Gem Trails, D. J. Henry, Gemac.

Colorado Gem Trails and Mineral Guide, R. M. Pearl, Sage Books; 1958.

Common Rocks and Minerals of Missouri, The, W. D. Keller, University of Missouri Bulletin, Vol. 52, No. 18, Missouri Handbook No. 1; Columbia; Revised Edition; 1951.

Connecticut Minerals, J. A. Sohon, Connecticut Geological and Natural History Survey Bulletin 77; Storrs; 1951.

Fossils in America, J. E. Ransom, Harper; 1964.

Gem Hunter's Guide, R. P. MacFall, Crowell Co.; 1963.

Gemstones of North America, J. Sinkankas, D. Van Nostrand; 1959.

Gem Trails of Texas, B. W. Simpson, Gem Trails; 1958.

Geology and Mineral Resources of North Carolina, J. L. Stuckey, North Carolina State Division of Mineral Resources, Educational Series 3; Raleigh; 1953.

Geology of New Hampshire, Part 3, Minerals and Mines, The, New Hampshire State Planning and Development Commission; Concord; 1956.

Guide to Some Minerals and Rocks in Indiana, S. S. Greenburg, W. M. Bundy, and D. J. McGregor, Indiana Department of Conservation, Geological Survey Circular 4; Bloomington; 1958.

Index to the Minerals and Rocks of Alabama, H. D. Pallister, Geological Survey of Alabama Bulletin 65; University; 1955.

Kansas Rocks and Minerals, L. L. Tolsted and A. Swineford, Kansas State Geological Survey; Lawrence; 1957.

List of Canadian Mineral Occurrences, A, R. A. A. Johnston, Canada Department of Mines, Geological Survey Memoir 74; 1915.

List of New York Mineral Localities, H. P. Whitlock, New York State Museum Bulletin 70, Mineralogy No. 3; Albany; 1903.

Maine Mineral Collecting, Maine Geological Survey, Department of Economic Development; Augusta; 1960.

Maine Pegmatite Mines and Prospects and Associated Minerals, Maine Geological Survey, Department of Development of Industry and Commerce Mineral Resources Index 1; Augusta; 1957.

Midwest Gem Trails, J. C. Zeitner, Gemac.

Mineral Occurrences of New York State with Selected References to Each Locality, U.S. Geological Survey Bulletin 1072 (F); 1959.

Mineralogical Journeys in Arizona, A. L. Flagg, F. H. Bitner; 1958.

Mineralogy of Kentucky, The, C. H. Richardson, Kentucky Geological Survey, Series 6, Geologic Reports, Vol. 33; Frankfort; 1925.

Mineralogy of Pennsylvania, S. G. Gordon, Academy of Natural Sciences of Philadelphia; Special Publication I, 1922. Reprinted.

Mineral Collecting in Pennsylvania, D. M. Lapham and A. R. Geyer, Pennsylvania Geological Survey Bulletin G-33; Harrisburg; 1959.

Mineral Collecting in Virginia, A. A. Pegau, Virginia Geological Survey, Virginia Minerals, Vol. 3, No. 2; Charlottesville; 1957.

*Mineral Localities of North Carolina*, J. F. Conley, North Carolina Division of Mineral Resources Information Circular 16; Raleigh; 1958. Very good.

*Mineral Resources of Minnesota*, W. H. Emmons and F. F. Grout, Minnesota Geological Survey Bulletin 30; Minneapolis; 1943.

*Mineral Resources of North Dakota, The*, C. E. Budge, North Dakota Research Foundation Bulletin 8; Bismarck; 1954.

*Mineral Resources of South Dakota*, South Dakota Natural Resources Commission; Pierre; 1952.

*Minerals of Arizona*, F. W. Galbraith and D. J. Brennan, University of Arizona Press; Tucson; Third Edition Revised; 1959.

*Minerals of the Black Hills, The*, V. Ziegler, South Dakota School of Mines, Department of Geology and Mineralogy Bulletin 10; Rapid City; 1914.

*Minerals of California*, J. Murdoch and R. W. Webb, California Division of Mines, Bulletin 173; San Francisco; 1956.

*Minerals of Idaho, The*, E. V. Shannon, U.S. National Museum Bulletin 131; Washington, D.C.; 1931.

*Minerals of Maryland*, C. W. Ostrander and W. E. Price, Natural History Society of Maryland; Baltimore; 1940.

*Minerals of New Jersey*, A. S. Wilkerson, Geological Society of New Jersey Report 1; State Museum; Trenton; 1959.

*Minerals of New Mexico*, S. A. Northrup, University of New Mexico Press; Albuquerque; Revised Edition; 1960.

*Minerals of Western Connecticut and Southeastern New York State, The*, R. V. Januzzi, Mineralogical Press, 83 Elm St., Danbury, Connecticut.

*New Mexico Gem Trails*, B. W. Simpson, Gemac.

*Nevada's Common Minerals*, V. P. Gianella, University of Nevada Bulletin, Vol. 35, No. 6, Geology and Mining Series 36; Reno; 1941.

*Northwest Gem Trails*, H. C. Dake, Gemac.

*Petrified Forest Trails*, J. E. Ransom, Gemac.

*Range Guide to Mines and Minerals, A*, J. E. Ransom, Harper; 1964.

*Rock Collector's Nevada and Idaho, The*, L. R. Gordon, Long Beach, California; 1953.

*Rock Hunter's Range Guide, The*, J. E. Ransom, Harper; New York; 1962.

*Rocks and Minerals of Michigan*, O. F. Poindexter, H. M. Martin, and S. G. Bergquist, Michigan Department of Conservation, Geological Survey Division, Publication 42; Lansing; Revised Edition; 1953.

*Treasure Map of the Great Mojave Desert*, M. F. Berkholz, Gemac.

*Typical Rocks and Minerals in Illinois*, G. E. Ekblaw and D. L. Carroll, Illinois Geological Survey, Educational Series 3; Urbana; 1931.

*Wyoming Mineral Resources*, F. W. Osterwald, Wyoming Geological Survey Bulletin 45; Laramie; 1952.

*Wyoming's Mineral Resources*, R. W. Birch, Wyoming Natural Resources Board; Laramie; 1955.

*Virginia Mineral Localities*, R. V. Dietrich, Virginia Polytechnic Institute, Engineering Experiment Station Series 88; Blacksburg; 1953.

*Virginia Minerals and Rocks*, R. V. Dietrich, Virginia Polytechnic Institute, Engineering Experiment Station Series 122; Blacksburg; 1958.

Gemac Corporation
P.O. Box 808, Mentone, California.

## GROUP D

ROCKS AND MINERALS MAGAZINES

*Desert Magazine*, Palm Desert, California. Articles on cutting and polishing gems and rocks, on collecting and field trips.

*Earth Science*, Box 550, Downers Grove, Illinois 60515. Popular articles covering all aspects of geology.

*Gems and Minerals*, Box 687, Mentone, California 92359. Many articles on cutting and polishing gems and rocks, on collecting and field trips.

*Lapidary Journal*, P. O. Box 2369, San Diego, California 92112. Articles about rock and gem cutting, mounting, jewelry settings. The special *Rockhound Buyer's Guide* issue (April, annually) is valuable (see Group B).

*Rocks and Minerals*, Box 29, Peekskill, New York 10566. Popular articles covering all aspects of geology.

**absolute age** The dating of an object of geologic importance in terms of years. Absolute age is determined in a laboratory. (See also RELATIVE AGE.)

**atom** A combination of protons and neutrons (forming the core, or nucleus) and one or more electrons circling the nucleus. (See diagrams on page 16.) Ninety-two kinds are found in nature; 103 kinds are now known.

**batholith** A huge mass of igneous rock that formed underground when a large body of magma solidified. As time goes on, erosion and gradual crustal uplift often expose such rock. A famous example of a large batholith now seen on the surface of the Earth are the Sierra Nevada Mountains along the California-Nevada border.

**bedding** In sedimentary rock the layering of clay, for instance, on top of sand and so on, producing a sandwich-like appearance. Bedding in sedimentary rock causes the rocks to split along the parallel planes.

**bedrock** The solid and continuous rock of the Earth's crust lying beneath the soil, or seen exposed on the surface.

**caldera** A very large and generally circular basin-shaped depression usually found at the top of a volcano. The diameter of the depression is more than three times the depth.

**cast** Any substance, such as a mineral, that has hardened after filling a mold formed by a shell, say, or some other animal or plant part (see MOLD; also see photo on page 96).

**cementation** During lithification (see LITH-IFICATION) certain binding materials act as a glue-like substance that holds together the individual particles making up the sediments.

**cleavage** The ability of many minerals to split in one or more directions along smooth plane surfaces. Cleavage is different from fracture.

**compound** Any substance made up of a chemical combination of two or more elements. Silicon dioxide, made up of one part

silicon and two parts oxygen, is an example of a compound called quartz.

**conchoidal fracture** The ability of a few minerals and rocks to fracture in such a way that rather smooth but curved surfaces resembling the inside of a shell are produced. Typical of the mineral chalcedony and the rock obsidian.

**conglomerate** Rounded large bits and pieces of rock that have been cemented together by mineral substances. (See photo on page 34.)

**contour interval** Difference in elevation between two adjacent contour lines.

**contour line** A specific line on a topographic map connecting all the points on the land surface which have the same elevation. The value of its elevation is usually not shown numerically (see INDEX CONTOUR).

**crystal** A naturally occurring solid, the form of which duplicates the regularly repeated fixed arrangement of the atoms forming the crystal (see photos on pages 20 and 21).

**desiccation** The process of drying up.

**dike** A long, wide, but thin body of intrusive igneous rock that cuts across the layering of the surrounding rock formation (see INTRUSION).

**electron** A negatively charged particle which forms part of an atom. Hydrogen, the simplest atom, has one electron. Heavier atoms have more than one electron.

**element** A distinctive combination of protons, neutrons, and electrons which cannot be broken down by ordinary chemical methods. The basic properties of an element are determined by its number of protons. Each element is identified by a number which is the same as its number of protons. Ninety-two different elements are found in nature; 103 elements are now known. The atoms of each element, such as gold, aluminum, and so on, are all alike.

**escarpment** The steep face or cliff formed where a high land area abruptly ends adjacent to a region of much lower elevations.

**extinction**  The total disappearance of an entire species or higher group of plants or animals.

**extrusion**  Molten rock that has spilled out onto the Earth's surface, such as a lava flow.

**felsic minerals**  (See NONFERROMAGNESIAN MINERALS.)

**ferromagnesian minerals**  A group of dark-colored and heavy common rock-forming silicate minerals containing iron and magnesium. Also called MAFIC MINERALS.

**float**  A term used to describe pieces of rock which have become detached and separated from the bedrock to which they belong. They lie scattered about on the surface of the land, usually at some distance from their source.

**fluorescence**  The glowing light given off by a few minerals when exposed to ultraviolet light.

**foliation**  In some metamorphic rock the visible layering caused by the parallel alignment of minerals. Usually the product of regional metamorphism (see METAMORPHIC ROCK).

**formation**  A "unit" of rock large enough to be shown on a geologic map. It has definite upper and lower edges (or contacts) and specific physical features such as kind of rock, color, fossil content, geologic age, and so on. From these features the rock may be traced from one area to another and, thereby, be distinguished from other formations. A formation is designated by two names—the geographical area where it was first described, followed either by the word "formation" or a one-word description of the rock type.

**fossils**  The remains of imprints of animals or plants that have been preserved in rocks and are more than 10,000 years old. (See photos on pages 86 to 97.)

**fracture**  The random and irregular way in which some minerals break. Fracture is different from cleavage.

**geologic cross-section**  A scaled diagram representing a vertical cut through part of the Earth's crust and showing the position, distribution, and arrangement of the rock formations underlying the surface of the land. (See also FORMATION.)

**geologic map**  A topographic map which shows the distribution, arrangement, and pattern of the rock formations at the surface. It also indicates the age of the formations and, by means of a cross section, their arrangement and distribution beneath the surface.

**geologic time**  The portion of time that took place before written history began. It involves a very long span of time, much longer than anyone can really imagine. (See the geologic time chart beginning on page 111.)

**hachure**  A short line drawn at right angles to a contour line to indicate a depression in the terrain.

**half-life**  The period of time during which one half of the number of atoms of a radioactive element change into atoms of a different element (see RADIOACTIVITY).

**hardness test**  The ability of a mineral to resist being scratched by minerals of different hardness. (See the Mohs Scale of Hardness on page 42.)

**heft**  (See SPECIFIC GRAVITY.)

**igneous rock**  Rock formed when molten material (see MAGMA and LAVA) flows up from deeper parts of the Earth's crust and solidifies either within the crust or at the surface.

**index contour**  Every fifth contour line on a topographic map is thicker than the intervening contour lines. Its elevation is usually shown numerically at several places along its course.

**intrusion**  Molten igneous rock that forces its way into the surrounding solid rock and solidifies below the Earth's surface.

**laccolith**  A mass of igneous rock that formed underground when a body of magma domed up the rock into which it was intruded and solidified. Eventually erosion exposes a laccolith (see diagram on page 28).

**lava**  Molten rock (magma) that is forced out of a volcano or out of cracks in the Earth's crust and onto its surface.

**lithification**  The process that turns sands, clays, and other sediments into solid rock. (See also CEMENTATION.)

**luster**  The way a mineral appears to shine in reflected light. Terms such as "metallic" and "glassy" are used to describe luster.

Luster does not depend on the color of the mineral.

**mafic minerals** (See FERROMAGNESIAN MINERALS.)

**magma** Fluid rock material originating in the deeper parts of the Earth's crust. It is capable of forcing its way up through solid rock and, when flowing out over the Earth's surface, it is then called lava.

**metamorphic rock** Any rock mass of the Earth's crust that has been recognizably changed in texture and/or mineral composition by heat or chemically active fluids, as in **contact metamorphism;** or by pressure at depth within the Earth's crust, as in **regional metamorphism.**

**mineral** Any element or compound found naturally in the Earth, formed by a non-living process, having a fairly uniform chemical composition and a rather constant set of physical properties, and having a fixed and orderly internal arrangement of its atoms.

**mold** A hollow impression preserved in rock and revealing the shape of a shell, for instance, or some other animal or plant part.

**neutron** A particle present in the nucleus of all atoms except hydrogen. Unlike electrons and protons, neutrons do not have an electrical charge. They simply add mass to an atom.

**nonferromagnesian minerals** A category of light-colored common rock-forming silicate minerals. They do not contain iron or magnesium. (Also, FELSIC MINERALS.)

**outcrop** Bedrock that is exposed to view. (See photo on page 75.)

**petrifaction** The process whereby water containing mineral matter replaces, particle by particle, the once-living tissues of plants and animals with the dissolved mineral matter. The resulting fossil is an exact solidified mineral replica of the original organic matter.

**proton** A positively charged particle present in the nucleus of all atoms.

**radioactivity** A few of the 103 known elements "decay" naturally, and in the process change into a different element. As they decay they emit some of the charged particles (protons) in their nuclei.

**relative age** The placement of a fossil, rock formation, or other object of geologic importance into its proper time relationship with other fossils, rock formations, and so on. Reference is not made to age in terms of number of years. (See ABSOLUTE AGE and also the geologic time chart beginning on page 111.)

**rock** A solid, naturally occurring mixture of minerals. Very often a rock is made up of minerals or other rock fragments and may contain the remains of once-living things.

**rock unit** (See FORMATION.)

**scale** Ratio of the distance between two points on the ground and the identical points on the map.

**sedimentary rock** Rock formed from clay, lime, sand, gravel—and sometimes plant and/or animal remains—that have been squeezed under great weight and pressure for long periods of time. Sedimentary rock make up about 75 percent of the land area of the world. (See also CEMENTATION, LITHIFICATION, and BEDDING.)

**silicate minerals** A group of minerals including more than half of all the known minerals. All contain oxygen, silicon, and one or more metals.

**sill** A long, wide but thin body of intrusive igneous rock that lies parallel to the layering of the surrounding rock formation (see INTRUSION). The famous Palisades of New Jersey-New York is a sill exposed by erosion.

**specific gravity** A number that represents the ratio between the weight of a given volume of a material and the weight of an equal volume of water. The higher the number the "heavier" the material.

**streak** The color of the powder trail a mineral leaves when it is rubbed over a piece of unglazed porcelain tile.

**texture** A term describing the appearance (size, shape, and arrangement) of the particles making up the rock.

**topographic map** A scaled map showing the position, relationship, size, and shape of all the physical features such as hills, valleys, roads, towns, and so on, of any given area of the Earth's surface.

124

# INDEX

## ABOUT THE AUTHORS

*Roy A. Gallant* has written many books and over 500 magazine articles, mostly on scientific subjects. In 1956 his book EXPLORING THE UNIVERSE won the Thomas Alva Edison Foundation Award for the best young people's science book of the year. He has worked on the staffs of *Science Illustrated, Boy's Life,* and *Scholastic Teacher.* Presently he is serving as consultant and author for a number of science education publishers and programs, including the Elementary School Science Project of the University of Illinois, and *Nature and Science,* The American Museum of Natural History.

*Christopher J. Schuberth* received his MS in Geology from New York University in 1960 and has been on the Staff of The American Museum of Natural History since 1957. He is a member of the geology department at Hunter College of the City University of New York and at Fairleigh Dickinson University. He has done extensive field work throughout the United States, particularly in Arizona, New York, and New Jersey. During the summer of 1960, he instructed a field course offered by the National Science Foundation for high school earth-science teachers in southeastern Arizona.

## ILLUSTRATION CREDITS

THE AMERICAN MUSEUM OF NATURAL HISTORY: pages 2, 18 (top), 20, 21, 33, 34, 40 (bottom left), 40 (bottom right), 41 (bottom right), 45 (top left), 49, 80, 88, 89, 92, 93, 95–97, 102–103, 105, 111. HARRIET COLE: pages 18 (bottom), 83 (bottom). ROY A. GALLANT: pages 15, 39, 41 (top left), 69 (bottom), 82, 83 (top four), 85, 91, 115. THE GRANGER COLLECTION: page 100. The artwork for this book was prepared by the Graphic Arts Division of The American Museum of Natural History; also by Juan Barberis, Gaetano Di Palma, Philip Lohman, and Joseph M. Sedacca: pages 12, 16, 18, 24, 28, 29, 32, 47, 56, 57, 71, 72, 74, 77, 81, 84, 89, 91, 94, 99 (bottom), 101, 104, 106, 108. HUMBLE OIL & REFINING COMPANY: page 70. JAPAN NATIONAL TOURIST ORGANIZATION: page 9. NATIONAL PARK SERVICE: pages 27 (William W. Dunmire), 30 (bottom, Menning), 37 (top, Palmer), 54, 63 (bottom), 67. PALISADES INTERSTATE PARK: page 68. PEABODY MUSEUM OF NATURAL HISTORY, YALE UNIVERSITY: pages 98–99 (top). JOHN POLGREEN: page 11. CHRISTOPHER J. SCHUBERTH: pages 37 (bottom), 60, 62, 64 (top), 65 (top and bottom), 66, 69 (top), 75, 79. JOHN S. SHELTON: pages 61, 64 (bottom). STANDARD OIL CO. (N. J.): page 10. UNION PACIFIC RAILROAD: page 63 (top). PAUL VILLIARD: pages 20, 30 (top), 40 (top), 41 (top right and bottom left), 42, 43, 44, 45 (top right and three photos at bottom), 46, 48, 86.

# Geologic Map of the Shooks Gap Quadrangle, Tennesse